Beautiful Heart, Beautiful Spirit

SHING-LING-MEI
WUDANG QIGONG

AS TAUGHT BY MASTER QING CHUAN WANG

By Katherine Orr

DragonGate Publishing

Layout and production by Angela Wu-Ki
Cover and interior artwork by Katherine Orr
Photos provided by Katherine Orr and the Wang family

Library of Congress Control Number: 2005902061

Orr, Katherine
BEAUTIFUL HEART, BEAUTIFUL SPIRIT
Shing-ling-mei Wudang Qigong as taught by Master Qing
Chuan Wang / Katherine Orr

ISBN 978-0-9765178-0-1

Printed in the United States of America

FIRST PRINTING

DragonGate Publishing
44-119 Bayview Haven Pl.
Kaneohe, HI 96744

ACKNOWLEDGMENTS

The network of people connected with this book stretches far and wide, spanning two continents. Many of your names I don't even know, and others I don't remember—but thank you all. If you had not played your parts as you did, Master Wang would not have made it to this country. And once arrived here, he wouldn't have stayed. Special thanks to those students on Kauai and Oahu who helped Master Wang get established during his transition to a new land: Blossom Cobb-Adams, Jack West, Marilyn Mach, Marie-Claude Wacker, Melanie Nagao, Chris Liu, Layton Chew and Keno Ravelo. Thank you, Gary Yoshida, for helping Master Wang through all those moves!

Thank you to the many qigong students and clients who have shared their personal stories with me, many of which have found their way into this book. Thank you, Haruko Cook and colleagues at the Department of East Asian Languages, University of Hawaii, for shedding light on the metaphor of qi in modern language. Thank you to Laura Duggan, Colleen Izutsu, Bill Orr, Bruce Mills, Ann Malo, Pamela Simon, Sharon Pang and others who took the time to give input and advice about the manuscript during different stages of its development.

A very special thank you to my tireless editor and long-time friend, Jude Berman. Without your expert navigational skills, patient direction and good humor, this book would not exist in its present form. You have made this writer's journey a pleasure.

And last but not least, my deepest thanks and appreciation go to the source of inspiration for this book: my dear husband, Qing Chuan. Without you, this book and so much more would not exist at all.

CONTENTS

PART FIVE The Exercises

FOREWORD

Beautiful heart, beautiful spirit! What a pleasure you have in store as you read and absorb the wisdom contained in this book. It is the heart offering of Master Qing Chuan Wang, containing the refined essence of his life's work and knowledge.

In the midst of the busyness and constant demands of daily life, we all feel the heart's longing to live with greater beauty, serenity and joy. This is the true human spirit. Shing-ling-mei Wudang qigong, described in this book, offers a gentle and effective means to allow spirit to shape our lives in a most beautiful way—a way that is open to all.

I was fortunate to meet Master Wang in the early 1990s in Hawaii, shortly after his arrival in the West from China. At the time, I was on a sabbatical from my teaching duties as a Siddha Yoga meditation monk, and was looking for a gentle "movement exercise" to keep my body flexible and strong, particularly as a support for my meditation practice. A friend of mine, who was a well-known physical therapist and healer in the area, recommended qigong and enthusiastically encouraged me to see Master Wang.

I went to my first qigong class just to observe, but as soon as Master Wang began to demonstrate the slow, graceful qigong movements, I knew I wanted to join in. As Master Wang moved, the room became still and filled with a healing energy. To my surprise and delight, something inside me instinctively understood what he was doing. It was as if my own life force, my *qi*, spoke up and said, "I know this. I want to do this. This will be good for me."

After completing his demonstration, Master Wang turned to the class, gave a big smile and said, "Now you do." He then guided the class with great care, showing us how to feel our own qi and move it through the body in the most beneficial way. For many, what had been a subtle concept of qi became a tangible experience. And from that experience sprang an even greater enthusiasm for the practice and a confidence in our own ability to heal and vitalize the body.

Over the past thirty years, I have been a keen student of *prana,* the subtle energy system described by the Indian yoga tradition. Through my friendship and association with Master Wang, I have learned so much about the profound science of qi. His knowledge of this field is absolutely thorough.

According to both the Indian and Chinese systems, physical disease, sluggishness and negative states of mind originate from a prolonged imbalance of the natural flow of subtle energy in the body. What a gift it would be to know how to monitor and regulate the subtle energy in our bodies to sustain good health. This is what a true qigong master, such as Master Wang, is able to teach. Over the past decade, as I have made occasional trips to Hawaii, I have seen his students progress in their practice. Now many are able to understand the natural flow of energy through their system, and with their Shing-ling-mei qigong practice move fresh qi through the body and release stagnant energy. In this way, they are able to strengthen and tone their internal organs, increase health and flexibility in their body and brighten their inner state. They can literally generate and hold a state of happiness and well-being.

Master Wang's students are people of all ages—teenagers to octogenarians—of all religions, occupations, races, shapes and sizes. It has been inspiring to see how qigong has benefited them all. I hold each one of them in the greatest respect, as I have seen them bring forth through their practice their own innate wisdom, greatness and graceful way of being.

I am so happy to see the publication of this book, which will be a boon to so many. The Chinese tradition of qigong is vast and ancient, going back millennia. It is an oral tradition, the wisdom of which has been kept alive, refined and passed on by its masters. Kathy Orr has rendered a great service in bringing forth this book. We owe her a huge vote of gratitude for going to the source—the living master of this lineage—and through her dedicated practice and inquiring mind, documenting, testing and clarifying the history and teachings of qigong for us.

Kathy is the perfect person to have written this book. She is one of Master Wang's most advanced students, and his wife and companion of many years. A scientist by profession, she asks the pertinent questions and explains with great clarity what qigong is, how it works and what its benefits are. As the author of numerous nature books for children, Kathy knows how to hold interest. Through anecdotes, personal history and a clear presentation of the philosophical principles, she has created a very readable narrative that presents an overview of the qigong tradition, as well as a thorough introduction to the form of qigong taught by Master Wang: Shing-ling-mei Wudang qigong.

May the love and wisdom contained in this book touch many hearts, uplift the spirit and bless our sacred world.

Swami Ishwarananda
First Day of Spring, 2004
Shree Muktananda Ashram
South Fallsburg, New York

AUTHOR'S NOTE

This book is written to inform and inspire. It is not intended to diagnose or prescribe. A qigong master is an energy specialist, not a medical doctor. Qigong should not be used as a replacement for professional medical advice. Rather, it serves as a powerful form of self-healing and a helpful adjunct to many forms of therapy, including Western medicine.

About the spelling—
Because the Chinese written language doesn't use the Roman alphabet, Western translators had to devise their own phonetic equivalents. Over the years, confusion ensued as translators from different countries adopted various spellings for the same Chinese words. In 1958, the People's Republic of China chose a system known as *pinyin* as their official means of writing in Roman letters. Since then, pinyin has been recognized as the international standard and is gradually replacing the previously popular Wade-Giles system of spelling. Although pinyin is not phonetically identical to English, it addresses the urgent need for standardization, and I have used it throughout this book. Therefore, "ch'i," (pronounced *chee*) is spelled *qi*, and "ch'i-kung" (pronounced *chee-GUNG*) is spelled *qigong*. How these words are pronounced remains unchanged.

Quick reference guide to spellings used in this book:

Pinyin	Wade-Giles
Dao, Daoist	Tao, Taoist
gong fu	kung fu
Lao Zi	Lao Tse
qi	chi
qigong	chi kung
Qing	Ching
taiji quan	tai chi chuan
Zhang San Feng	Chang San Feng

The one exception to pinyin in this book is the first word in the name of the form of qigong Master Wang teaches, called Shing-ling-mei. The word for "heart" in pinyin is pronounced *shing* but spelled *xin*. To ease the way for those who aren't yet familiar with pinyin spelling, we have chosen to follow ears instead of eyes on this one.

INTRODUCTION

Almost as soon as Master Qing Chuan Wang began teaching qigong in Hawaii in 1992, his students began asking for a book that contains information about qigong in general, and about Master Wang's style and teachings in particular. They wanted to know where qigong comes from, how old the practice is, what qigong can and can't do, and how long it takes to develop personal qigong ability. This book is written, in part, to answer their questions.

It has another audience in mind, as well. In my years together with Master Wang, I have seen many different kinds of people express profound gratitude for his work. Newcomers arrive, often having heard only that their friends' health and well-being improved through qigong. New clients sometimes get up from a qi balancing session, their eyes wide with wonder, and exclaim, "Wow, I feel so wonderful! What *was* that?" They want to frame their experience in a context they can understand. So this book is also intended to introduce qigong to newcomers such as these, who have yet to explore—or are on the threshold of discovering—the positive difference qigong can make in their lives.

These days, Western science and health have awakened to, and begun to embrace, the many psychological and health benefits of ancient arts of the Far East. Taiji, yoga, meditation and now qigong are becoming a part of mainstream culture. As such, qigong attracts a very broad following. Qigong practitioners come from virtually every ethnic and cultural background, every profession and socioeconomic group. They are young and old, healthy and infirm. Some have been attracted to qigong through stories of practitioners with exceptional abilities; they may have experienced certain energy phenomena themselves and come seeking answers or guidance. Others want to find a pragmatic, reliable practice to improve their health and daily functioning. There is room for everyone, and one approach does not negate or invalidate another.

In the first three chapters of this book, I describe how I encountered qigong, and the impact it has made on my life. You will learn about basic principles of qi and qigong, and get a glimpse into qi's place in world culture and a sense of qigong's emerging role in Western health science. In chapters four through six, you will read about Master Wang's life growing up in Shanghai, and become familiar with qigong's origins and recent history. In chapters seven, eight and nine, you will be introduced to Shing-ling-mei Wudang qigong. You will learn about Master Wang's core teachings and discover why he calls his practice Shing-ling-mei, or "beautiful heart, beautiful spirit." You will discover the profound practice and results of emitted qi therapy, or what Master Wang calls *qi balancing*. In chapters ten and eleven, you will learn how to make the most of qigong in your daily life and about the benefits experienced by Master Wang's students. In chapter twelve, you will share a dialog with Master Wang that serves to summarize key points. Peppered throughout the book are examples and stories of how qigong has helped people's lives.

The last section of the book is designed to help you get started with your own practice of Shing-ling-mei. You will be guided through some basic principles of practice and simple routines that can start you on your way. These exercises form a solid foundation of practice. By dedicating yourself to practicing these exercises, you can develop your qi and reap significant health benefits.

Shing-ling-mei Wudang qigong is a practice that is "all gain and no pain." In fact, if you're feeling pain as a result of your practice, you are doing something wrong. Shing-ling-mei is not about forcing anything, either mentally or physically. Instead, it allows you to tune into and cultivate the extremely pleasurable and satisfying sensation of balanced life-energy flowing through the body. It is about relaxing, releasing, opening and becoming present. It is about being quiet and tranquil and making happiness your friend.

"Shing-ling-mei Wudang qigong" might sound like quite a mouthful, but don't let that daunt you. You don't need to know a lot of strange terms or facts to do this practice well. In fact, qigong isn't something you learn intellectually. Like learning to swim, it must be directly experienced. It is a living process that uplifts and inspires, heals and refreshes, balances and renews. It has the potential to transform your life. How far you go with it is up to you.

To help this learning process come alive for you, I have drawn upon the experiences of Master Wang's students, as well as my own experiences acquired during thirteen years as Master Wang's student, assistant and wife. If this book serves to inform, educate, uplift or inspire you about the subject of qigong, it will have fulfilled its purpose. If your reading stimulates further questions and comments, please send them along. I welcome your input.

PART ONE WEST MEETS EAST

CHAPTER I

The Dance of Qi

Imagine you can feel the power of the universe as a pervasive, nourishing energy—an energy so complete that it sustains your very life, much like the air you breathe. Imagine you can use this living energy to transform your life for the better. What if you could use the energy of the mountains, the ocean and the sun to revitalize yourself? What if you could work with living energy to improve your health and melt away stress, uplift your mood and relieve pain? Suppose you could use it to find inspiration and new insights, and to help others heal.

Though it may sound like pure fantasy, this energy is very real, and many ordinary people work with it to achieve the benefits I just described. These benefits are the fruit of an ancient Chinese practice called *qigong*. For a growing number of people, myself included, qigong has become a cherished tool of daily life.

I first read about qigong in the science section of *The New York Times*, back in the mid 1980s. My eye was drawn to an article about a Chinese doctor who projected a "vital force" that his patient was able to feel without physical contact. The man was a qigong master, and he used this force to help his patient overcome paralysis. At the time, I was a practicing marine biologist and writer of children's nature books. I was so intrigued by the article that I clipped it and filed it.

Six years passed before I saw the word *qigong* again, this time on the front page of the *Kauai Times*. A cover story explained that a top qigong master from China had arrived in my backyard—the small island of Kauai, Hawaii—to introduce an ancient Chinese healing art called *qigong*. In China, Master Wang was licensed by the government to teach qigong and train qigong teachers. His own training in qigong and related healing arts had begun in childhood. These practices had been passed down for generations within his family in traditional Chinese custom. By age thirty-seven, he had become the 18th patriarch of Wudang qigong, the foremost lineage of Daoist qigong in China.

Again, I clipped the article… and this time quickly signed up for class.

EMBRACING THE QI

Over the years, I had taken many classes that taught gentle forms of stretching and movement for health. These classes focused on outer form—how to arch the back or tuck in the pelvis and distribute the weight between one foot and the other. Master Wang's qigong class was decidedly different. Although we were moving our bodies in specific ways, his class focused on *inner* movement. Through an English translator, he instructed us to use our minds and intention to move life energy, called *qi*, through our bodies and exchange it with nature. Most of us didn't know what qi was or how to feel it. But that didn't matter. Until we could truly feel the qi, we were encouraged to simply relax and imagine how it would feel if we *could* feel it.

Class was held outdoors in Hanalei, on a grassy lawn facing the mountains. Following the movements of our teacher, we opened our arms wide and gathered qi from the earth and sky. As I welcomed the energies of nature into my embrace, I was reminded of my early childhood, when I used to lie in the warm grass, arms splayed, staring at the sky. I used to pretend I was looking down into a bottomless ocean of sky, while the earthly sphere above held me close and safe. I loved the feeling of being held "under the earth's belly," along with all the little trees and houses, without the slightest fear of falling off into that deep, infinite blue. Without realizing it at the time, I was feeling the earth as a nurturing mother.

Now, with slow, graceful movements, the other students and I gathered nurturing qi energy from the mountains and sky and washed it gently through our bodies. The instructions were simple since Master Wang spoke just three words of English: *relax*, *open* and *smile*. Yet he embodied these words as he encouraged us to follow his movements.

Following Master Wang was like following silk wafting on a gentle breeze. This tall, smiling man must have weighed about two hundred pounds, yet he moved with surprising lightness and fluidity, as if his joints held some secret lubricant. Furthermore, he looked to be about thirty years old, though we had been told he was almost fifty. Lucky genes? Or was this the result of his qigong practice? I had no idea, but one thing was clear: by the end of the first class I felt deliciously relaxed, joyful and refreshed.

I began to attend classes several times a week, and with each experience I found myself growing more intrigued by this mysterious thing called *qi*.

Each practice session left me with a warm afterglow and a sense of replenishment. Although I still had just a vague idea of what qi was and what it felt like, I found I kept thinking of Linus, Charlie Brown's little friend who carries his blanket with him throughout the *Peanuts* cartoon strip. The waves of qi I was learning to wash through my body reminded me of Linus's blanket—so comforting and nurturing. Yet even better than being wrapped in a cuddly blanket, I felt permeated by it!

THE MYSTERY OF QI

One evening Master Wang gave a demonstration of qigong at the local hospital. After performing a series of beautiful qigong movements that looked like a graceful dance done in very slow motion, he projected qi energy to volunteers from the audience. As each volunteer sat in a chair at the front of the room, Master Wang slowly moved his hands in the air along the volunteer's arm or leg, as if pushing and pulling against an invisible sleeve surrounding the limb.

From my seat in the audience, I suddenly realized I was watching a scenario almost identical to the one I had read about in *The New York Times* article many years earlier. As the demonstration progressed, a translator explained that qigong was a form of traditional Chinese healing, and that Master Wang could project his own qi and use it to stimulate the qi inside another person's body. The exact nature of qi was something of a mystery, he said, but mysterious or not, it was known to work.

A fellow qigong student said to me later, "I was sitting in the audience when I noticed some kind of ripples in the air around Master Wang's body. I missed everything else about the demonstration from then on because I was so intrigued by whatever I was seeing. Waves were coming off his back like heat waves rising from a toaster, and I could watch this from my seat clear across the room."

As for myself, I was focused on the volunteers, watching intently for their reactions. Some seemed not to feel much of anything, while others reported distinct, even strong, sensations that elicited smiles and expressions of amazement and surprise. I looked forward to the time when I would experience this "qi treatment" for myself, and wondered if some day we students would be able to work with our own qi, and the qi of others, in this astounding way.

WHAT IS QI?

So, what *is* qi? The straightforward answer is this: Qi is the Chinese word for life force, or life energy. It is the vital force that allows us to think and act; it is the force that gives us life. When our qi is gone, we are dead.

You can think of qi as both a form of life-giving electricity that flows throughout the body and the force field it generates. Like the electrical "juice" of life, it sustains every tissue and cell. According to traditional Chinese medicine, it is the flow of this current as well as the qualities of its flow that sustain our physical health and impart a sense of emotional well-being and mental clarity. If qi were a river, then the nature of its flow might be choppy or smooth, turbid or clear, a trickle or torrent.

Qi also means air and breath. Breathing is our most intimate and ongoing exchange with the world around us. Like the flow of qi, breathing is so necessary for life that we can't survive long without it. Still, qi is neither the air we breathe nor the act of breathing, but the life energy inherent in these. It is more accurate to think of qi as the "breath of life."

Qi is more than this, as well. Qi is the animating force behind all of nature. According to ancient Chinese philosophy, we are part of a living universe that is sustained and driven by the flowing presence of qi. All forms of nature—from toadstools to stars, as well as the earth's forces, weather patterns and movements of the cosmos—arise as ever-changing expressions of the continually flowing, transforming dance of qi.

WHERE IS QI?

As my awareness and understanding of qi increased, so did my appreciation of its pervasive presence in nature. Looking around at the islands where I live, I began to perceive qi as the unifying force behind all life, creating nature's ever-changing landscape from behind the scenes. Hawaii's once barren lava mountains have become lush and bursting with life, as qi expresses itself in physical forms. Old plants wither and die as life force slowly ebbs from them like a receding tide, while elsewhere green shoots burst forth as life extends its vibrant fingers of qi in new directions.

Throughout nature, millions of systems operate within larger systems. They integrate seamlessly with one another and combine to form the giant system we call our earth. Earth, in turn, has its place within our solar system and the larger systems of our galaxy and universe. Earth's systems are so complex that scientists are still struggling to understand how they work, yet their innate ability to self-regulate and perpetuate has sustained life on earth for eons without the help of a single human being. This same power of intelligence is at work in our body. Without having to understand how it happens, our body heals itself. Our bones mend, hair grows. A myriad of necessary reactions regulates our body's chemistry in each moment, maintaining a dynamic equilibrium that allows life to flourish. According to ancient Chinese philosophy, this is all an expression of the eternal dance of qi.

So, where is qi? It is in our heart as it beats, in our blood as it flows. It is in the waves that pound on the beach, in the river that empties into the sea. It is in the clouds drifting in the sky, and in the sky itself. It is with qi that we run a marathon, and with qi that we blink an eye. In this universe as in our own bodies, the subtle but wondrous energy of qi is running the whole show.

TRACKS OF QI

During those first months of qigong class, each week held some new surprise. I felt as if I were on the trail of some mysterious and elusive animal, as skeptic and believer traded places from moment to moment within myself. The scientist in me still needed to know something was happening physiologically, that it wasn't all "just in my mind." And each class held some surprising new proof.

During class one evening, we were outdoors beneath the full moon, gathering "moon qi." Suddenly, I noticed a unique sensation like little ants crawling under the skin in the center of my palms! Master Wang, through the translator, explained that this was a normal qi sensation. At the center of each palm is an energy gateway, where qi is absorbed and released. I was merely feeling the sensation of qi as it entered that gateway.

On another occasion, we were doing a sweeping movement with one arm, gathering qi from nature and bringing it to our feet. As I scooped my left arm around and brought my palm down toward my leg, I was astonished to feel a spray of tingles radiate outward from my shin. "Golly," I thought. "Did *I* do that?" It felt as if I had splashed something onto it, only the splash was not a concrete substance—it was the subtle sensation of qi.

Within weeks of starting qigong practice, five benign skin growths I'd had on my shins for years suddenly fell off, leaving smooth skin behind. Other students with more significant health problems were experiencing more dramatic healings, including freedom from chronic neck pain and back pain. One student found relief from chronic PMS, while another felt more grounded and self-confident.

We didn't understand much of what was happening to us because it was all so new and we couldn't easily converse with our teacher, but we laughed a lot as we exchanged stories about our experiences. We all agreed that Master Wang's qigong classes made us feel light-hearted and happy. Was this an effect of the qi? We also noticed that, even though we couldn't communicate well with Master Wang in words, he had an uncanny ability to "read our qi" and know a lot about what was going on with us, as well as help us learn to guide our qi. We were full of questions and delighted in each new surprise that unfolded along the way. I suspected there were bigger surprises still to come, as indeed there were.

CHAPTER 2

The Culture and Science of Qi

Life energy, in one form or another, is recognized by cultures around the world. Because life energy is invisible and inaudible to most people, it is not surprising that interpretations of what it is and how it works aren't entirely consistent from culture to culture, or even among individuals within a culture. Thus, the terms may vary slightly in meaning from one culture to the next, yet all carry the understanding of life force or spirit energy or the breath of life. Here are some examples:

> In China it is *qi*.
> In Japan it is *ki*.
> In India it is *prana* and *shakti*.
> In parts of Africa it is *ashe*.

To Hawaiians it is *ha* and *mana*.
To Native Americans it is *Great Spirit*.
To Christians it is the *Holy Spirit*.
To the ancient Egyptians it was *ka*.
To the ancient Greeks it was *pneuma*.

And in the West these days it is referred to by such terms as *bioenergy*, *bioelectricity*, *vital energy* and *vital force*.

THE LANGUAGE OF QI

For people in China and Japan, the understanding of qi is inherent in their language. Whether or not they are consciously aware of qi or its presence in their life, they use the word many times as a metaphor in the course of daily speech and writing.

Chinese characters	meaning	literal translation
天 氣	weather	heaven qi
元 氣	health	original qi
淘 氣	mischievous	impish qi
和 氣	friendly	peaceful qi
怒 氣	in a rage	qi is very upset
朝 氣	aggressive, exuberant	sparks of qi
漏 氣	to leak away	qi goes outside
精 氣	vitality	high quality qi
空 氣	the atmosphere	sky qi
香 氣	aroma	qi is fragrant

Japanese characters	meaning	literal translation
気 に 入 る	I *like* this	this gets into my qi
気 を 付 け る	to attract attention	to pull qi
気 を 失 う	to become unconscious	to lose qi
気 が 済 む	to feel satisfied	qi is satisfied
気 持 ち が い い	I feel good	how I hold qi is good
気 を 揉 む	I'm worried	I'm rubbing qi
気 軽	lighthearted or easy	qi is light
気 が 変 わ る	I change my mind	qi is changed
気 が 狂 う	to become crazy	qi is crazy
気 が 抜 け る	to be discouraged or dispirited	qi is pulled out

While most Asian people give little thought to the qi in their daily phrases, traditional Chinese healing methods, which work directly with qi, have developed an immense descriptive vocabulary over time. Traditional Chinese medicine identifies more forms of qi than the Eskimos have words for snow. Some forms of qi are defined by their function; other forms by their qualities. There is the qi we are born with and the qi we derive from food. There is the qi that runs our metabolism and the qi that protects us from external harm. There is the qi outside our body and the qi within. As part of qigong practice we learn to consciously replace "bad" qi—qi that is old, stale, stagnant or toxic—with "good" qi that is new, fresh and nourishing to the body.

Some Different Kinds of Qi

- Yuan qi, or natal qi—qi we're born with
- Hou tian qi or postnatal qi—qi we absorb during our lifetime from food, water, air, qigong practice
- Nei qi or internal qi—qi existing within the body
- Wai qi or external qi—qi emitted from the body

While a working knowledge of the many faces of qi is mandatory for those who want to understand traditional Chinese medicine, we don't need to know a lot of terms and definitions in order to practice qigong. Master Wang made it clear from the start that it is the experience of qi that counts, not an intellectual understanding of it. He pointed out that all the knowledge in the world *about* qigong cannot replace the essential process of *doing* it. For only by experiencing the feelings and effects of qi for ourselves do we directly come to know its reality.

FEELING THE QI

So what does qi feel like? While all new practitioners feel qi in their own way and at their own pace, my own experience was typical of many. I first felt qi as a subtle tingling sensation in my hands. This progressed gradually to a similar feeling in my feet, forearms and shins. Next I began to feel it more distinctly in my torso as a sense of pressure like a flowing wave.

Qi can feel warm or cool, heavy or buoyant, tingling or magnetic, flowing or electrical. One can feel all of these sensations at different times. However, these words don't tell the whole story because they don't describe the mood shift of overall well-being that accompanies practice. The overall effect of feeling qi is deeply satisfying and pleasurable. Relaxed, fulfilled, intoxicated, energized, centered and buoyant are terms that come to mind. In our Kauai class we used to describe ourselves as "drunk on qi."

This overall sense of well-being is usually quick to manifest, while the ability to feel qi moving under the guidance of one's intent generally takes more time to develop. I'd been practicing qigong for about a year when I finally noticed it. I was in the grocery store, of all places. As I walked up and down the aisles, I imagined I was leading qi up and down, up and down, between my neck and abdomen. I was in a pleasantly relaxed state, scanning the shelves for food items on sale, when I suddenly noticed it felt as though I were moving an invisible balloon up and down inside my body and I could control it at will. I was elated!

ENERGETIC ESSENCE

Master Wang explained that all of humanity walks between earth and sky, surrounded by the abundance and diversity of life. Each form of life—as well as earth, sky and other manifestations of nature—carries its own energetic essence, its own form of qi. We can use these different essences to balance, nourish and cleanse our body on the energetic level, just as we use food, water and medicine on the physical level.

During class, Master Wang often directed us to gather the different energies of sky qi, earth qi and ocean qi, and wash them through our body. I didn't pay much attention to these different forms of qi because all qi felt the same to me. In truth, I thought I was doing darn well just to feel qi. So I was surprised, one day, when Master Wang asked me if I could feel the difference between earth, sky and ocean qi.

When I said no, he told me to sit down and relax. I did so, and watched him close his eyes and begin to move his arms in the air. He stood at my side, making motions as if he were sweeping together an invisible pile of rice. He was gathering qi. When he had gathered enough, he said, "Earth qi." And he dumped it on my head like an unseen cloud, fluttering his fingers slightly in the air as he brought it down into my body. I felt a pleasant wave of qi—generic, of course; how else was qi supposed to feel? I became as quiet and alert as I could, dubious that I would be able to distinguish one kind of qi from another, even with his help.

Next he repeated these motions and announced, "Ocean qi." Again I felt a subtle wave of qi flood my body. But as I observed it with relaxed attention, I noticed that this wave felt slightly more viscous and cooler than the earth qi I had just experienced. Then came "sky qi." This time I noticed a distinctly open, radiant quality that had something of a buzz. I laughed in amazement at Master Wang's improbable demonstration. The energetic qualities I had just felt defied words because English doesn't include a descriptive vocabulary for energy, yet each felt like the energetic equivalent of what my senses ordinarily perceived.

Quantum physics tells us that we live in a world of energy fields. Our five senses translate the energy frequencies of our world into the sounds, textures, colors and objects that are familiar to us. My intellectual mind knew this from books, but when I felt those different forms of qi, I experienced the truth of this in a strange and immediate way.

THE SCIENCE OF QI

Although qi has been known since the dawn of history, it hasn't been recognized by modern scientific culture. Rather, it has been regarded as something ethereal and mysterious, belonging to the realm of mystics and the world of spirit. In modern society, where science has become the yardstick by which we measure truth, qi has until recently been something of a square peg among round holes.

Medical doctors and institutions look to scientific research for answers about what works and has value for their patients. For them to take qigong seriously, scientific research must show that it is a significant tool for health. Can qigong stand up to scientific scrutiny? Indeed it can.

In 1971, while in Beijing with U.S. officials preparing for President Nixon's visit, noted political analyst and *New York Times* reporter James Reston underwent an emergency appendectomy. Acupuncture (which manipulates qi with the aid of very fine needles) was used to treat his postoperative pain, and his account of the experience appeared on the front page of the *Times*. During Nixon's visit the following year, the President's personal physician observed doctors in hospitals performing surgery, using acupuncture as an anesthetic. The publicity arising from these events helped stimulate Western interest and research into the electrical nature of the human body and, more specifically, into the medical benefits of working with qi.

Since the 1980s, qigong has been the subject of extensive scientific inquiry in China, the United States and elsewhere around the globe. Because qigong is used in Chinese hospitals, both on its own and as an adjunct to other treatments, numerous studies employing scientific methods have yielded a wealth of evidence to validate the positive effects of qigong on health and healing. Researchers have tested people who practice qigong on themselves, as well as qigong masters who send qi into other people and into such objects as plants, animals, cells *in vitro* and assorted chemical substances, including perfume.

The results have been amazing. Aside from its many benefits to human health, some of which are listed below, the evidence shows that what the Chinese call qi—subtle energy directed by the mind—can stimulate the activity of enzymes in test tubes, kill tumor cells in petri dishes, stimulate the growth of plants, alter the structure of liquids and accelerate the rate of healing in animals. By demonstrating that qi can significantly affect non-human and non-living matter, the experimental evidence rules out the possibility that these effects are only the result of the recipients' expectations.

In the arena of human health, scientific research has demonstrated repeatedly that qigong combined with Western medicine can do significantly better than Western medicine alone. One of the best-known clinical studies was conducted at the Shanghai Institute of Hypertension, Shanghai 2nd Medical University, and was exemplary both for its long duration (30 years) and large number of participants (242 patients). In this study, which examined the effects of qigong on hypertension (high blood pressure), 242 patients, all on standard drug medication for high blood pressure, were divided into two groups: 122 patients practiced qigong while the remaining 120 did not. At the end of thirty years, 48% of the non-qigong group had died, while only 25% of those practicing qigong had died. While 41% of the non-qigong group suffered strokes during the study, only 20% of the qigong group did. And while 32% of the non-qigong group died from strokes, just 16% of the qigong group did. Additionally, medical examinations by ultrasound on 40 of these patients revealed that those who practiced qigong had stronger heart muscles.

Another study, conducted at the Kuangan Men Hospital in Beijing, examined the effects of qigong on 123 patients with advanced cancer. All the patients received standard cancer drug therapies, but 97 of them practiced qigong for two hours every day, while 30 did not. After approximately three months, 82% of the patients who practiced qigong regained strength, compared with 10% of the non-qigong group. While 63% of the qigong group experienced improved appetite, only 10% in the non-qigong group did. While 33% of the qigong group became free of diarrhea and other defecation irregularities, only 6% of the non-qigong patients did. White blood cell activity and red blood cell sedimentation rate—both indicators of immune function—

improved significantly in the qigong group, but improved little or diminished in the group that didn't practice qigong.

The many scientific and medical studies performed in the last twenty years are too numerous to recount, so I have summarized some of qigong's scientifically documented health benefits in the following list. Qigong has been shown to:

- strengthen the heart
- regulate blood pressure
- improve blood circulation
- build the immune system
- calm the nervous system
- increase lung efficiency
- enhance digestion and gastrointestinal tract function
- stimulate nerve regeneration
- normalize cells and tissues
- correct spinal problems
- improve function of vital organs
- shrink tumors
- stimulate enzymes
- raise IQ levels

Although this list is by no means complete, it conveys a sense of qigong's broad applications. This does not imply that qigong can heal everyone. Nothing can. Rather, it demonstrates that qigong is a science that can produce statistically significant, replicable results. For those of you who are interested in reviewing the evidence directly, I recommend the *Qigong Database*, a computerized collection of the abstracts of more than two thousand research studies compiled by Kenneth Sancier, Ph.D. For a predigested and readable presentation of the evidence, I recommend Kenneth S. Cohen's *The Way of Qigong*.

With so much evidence pointing to the effectiveness of qigong, the quest is on to determine what qi is in Western scientific terms, and how it works. Some scientists call qi a form of bioelectromagnetic energy (an energy with electrical and magnetic properties found in living organisms), but this is just a partial description of its correlates. Modern instruments have identified numerous correlates of qi that are emitted from the hands of qigong masters. These include low frequency sound waves, luminescence, static electricity and electromagnetic waves, such as ultra-violet, infra-red and microwaves. How does this information further the big picture?

Throughout history, significant discoveries have lain dormant for centuries until science developed a context in which to insert the new information. Facts that have no place within the existing paradigm of the day get swept aside until the accumulated pile becomes too large to ignore, whereupon a new framework of understanding is devised to accommodate them. For example, phenomena such as telepathy, the power of prayer and energy healing have been rejected repeatedly despite an abundance of impressive scientific documentation because their existence seems so foreign to prevailing scientific theory.

Happily, this is changing. Modern physics is developing a new scientific paradigm that embraces these phenomena. According to this paradigm, we live in a holographic universe where all points in space and time share interconnected and instantaneous communication. Energy conveys information, and the instant exchange of information on an energetic level gives rise to our physical world. With this new view, Western science moves toward Eastern mysticism, and the way is paved for deeper understanding of the phenomenon of qi and the practice of qigong. If you are interested in reading more about these ideas, I recommend *Nature's Mind: the Quantum Hologram*, a paper by former astronaut Edgar Mitchell, and *Science and Human Transformation (Subtle Energies, Intentionality and Consciousness)*, a book by William Tiller, Professor Emeritus of physics at Stanford University.

Modern Science and Qi

Do you remember how electrical currents and unseen waves were laughed at? The knowledge about man is still in its infancy. —Albert Einstein

Established ways of thinking die hard. An ancient Egyptian, Eratosthenes of Cyrene (circa 200 B.C.E.), proved scientifically that the earth was round by employing the sun, two obelisks and trigonometry. Nevertheless, much of the European community, led by the Catholic church, persistently maintained the earth was flat. Only after Magellan circumnavigated the globe in 1522 did they reluctantly change their view.

Today, most people's view of the world is based on theories and discoveries that are over three hundred years old. The last scientific revolution began in 1543, after Copernicus published his (at that time, radical) theory that the earth revolves around the sun. Since the late 1600s, the prevailing worldview has followed Sir Isaac Newton's concepts of classic physics, whereby our entire view of reality is based on just the limited fraction of the world we can perceive with our physical senses.

Technology and mathematics have advanced considerably in the last century, enabling scientists to examine the universe on an extremely tiny scale. At this level, the "laws of nature" with which we are familiar do not apply. For example, a sub-atomic particle can be in more than one place at the same time, and can vanish in one place and appear in another instantaneously. This is the realm of quantum physics, hailed as offering the most complete portrait of our universe yet devised. Scientists conversant with quantum physics can examine levels of energy function beyond the space-time continuum and explore the nature of energies that help form our manifest world.

Although scientists can directly detect qi's physical correlates (heat, electromagnetic waves, sound waves, luminescence, etc.), the nature of qi itself remains elusive. Like the mind, qi doesn't reside within the limits of the world we physically perceive, but acts upon it from subtler realms. Quantum physics has opened new doors of inquiry into these realms, but many unanswered questions and differing interpretations of findings remain to be explored. This makes exciting work for those who want to help expand scientific understanding of our universe and ourselves.

READING ABOUT THE SCIENCE OF QI

Cohen, Kenneth S, *The Way of Qigong*, New York: Ballantine Books, 1997.

Mitchell, Edgar, Nature's Mind: the Quantum Hologram,
International Journal of Computing Anticipatory Science, Vol. 7, 2000, and
http://www.edmitchellapollo14.com/naturearticle.htm.

The Qigong Database, The Qigong Institute, 561 Berkeley Ave., Menlo Park,
CA 94025, and http://www.qigonginstitute.org.

Tiller, William A, Ph.D., *Science and Human Transformation (Subtle energies,
Intentionality and Consciousness)*, Walnut Creek, CA: Pavior Publishing, 1997.

CHAPTER 3

Working with Qi

Four months after my first qigong class, Hurricane Iniki ravaged Kauai, turning the green landscape ash gray in a matter of hours as it shattered the tops of forests and houses across the island. My qigong practice became a wellspring of peace in Iniki's wake, as well as during other personally trying times that followed. I knew I had found a practice for life—one that could fill me with comfort and inner joy despite outer circumstances, and that allowed me to grow in seemingly limitless ways. I felt that qigong opened my heart to an extraordinary degree, encouraging me to tap new levels of awareness. I became less attached to the outer forms of life and more focused on its essence. You could say I fell in love with the benevolent essence of life itself, expressed as the inner intelligence and flow of qi. I fell in love, too, with the kindhearted Chinese man who always put the welfare of others first. Romance between us bloomed, and we eventually married.

In 2001, my husband took me to visit China for the first time. At last I saw for myself what I'd heard him describe so often. China's gardens and parks are full of people practicing simple forms of qigong. Everywhere I looked, people were strolling and standing, waving their arms, rolling their torsos and swaying their bodies.

I was immediately struck by qigong's great accessibility. Here were people from all walks of life and many different ages and backgrounds, all practicing qigong. Sometimes prospective students ask, "Do I have to be Chinese to practice qigong?" or "Do I have to give up my religion for qigong to work?" The answer to both questions is no. People of every race, culture, ethnic background, social class, gender, nationality and profession can practice qigong effectively. Qigong is not a religion, and people of all faiths can practice it. It can be practiced alongside other healing modalities and it doesn't conflict with any medications. Moreover, people can practice qigong at virtually any age, from ten to one hundred.

As we walked in the park, I saw a man bending over near a large bush to inhale qi from some freshly crushed leaves. Further along, a woman was shaking her hands at a small shrub. When I asked what she was doing, my husband explained that people and plants enjoy a reciprocal relationship in which each can use the other's waste for nourishment. In the same way that plants can utilize and transform the wastes from our digestion and respiration, they can also absorb and transform our "stagnant" qi—qi that is no longer helpful to our body. This woman was eliminating stagnant qi from her fingers, perhaps from arthritic joints.

The practice of qigong was not limited to parks, either. We were walking through the streets of Shanghai one day, when a loud slapping sound caught my attention. I turned to see an elderly man standing on the sidewalk just swaying his hips and slapping his buns! I was delighted to see these simple forms of qigong so accepted as a part of everyday life. In fact, today millions of people in China practice some form of qigong daily to help their general health, to balance and strengthen their body's internal systems and to relieve stress and pain.

DEFINING QIGONG

Qigong is composed of two words, *qi* and *gong*. *Qi,* as I explained in the previous chapter, is the Chinese word for "life energy" and refers to the energy that flows through the universe, as well as the energy that gives each of us life. *Gong* is short for *gong fu,* which literally means "energy time" or "work time." It refers to work, skill or expertise that is acquired gradually through practice and perseverance. Although we tend to associate gong fu specifically with the martial arts, it actually applies to any discipline or training that takes time and patience to master. For example, if I ask, "How is your piano gong fu?" or "How is your golf gong fu?" I'm referring to your level of mastery derived through your study and practice of that skill.

Simply defined, *qigong* means "working with life energy," or one's ability to work with life energy. In popular usage, qigong refers to the practice of working with *human* life energy. By practicing qigong, we learn to cultivate qi, the vital energy that permeates and empowers our bodies. The Chinese speak of qigong as a means of cultivating qi, implying a practice that takes time and cannot be rushed.

Yet to call qigong "a practice" is not entirely accurate. It is actually a diverse collection of energy practices that cultivate qi in different ways for specific purposes. There are *hard, external* styles that are used mainly for sports, showmanship and self-defense, as well as *soft, internal* styles that focus mainly on health and spiritual development. Despite their many differences, the vast majority of qigong forms are safe to practice and extremely beneficial in terms of improving health, enhancing well-being and calming emotions.

A PRACTICE FOR ALL SEASONS

As we strolled the streets of Old Shanghai, dappled by sunlight filtering down through the leafy canopy of sycamore trees, my husband led me to the park where he used to practice with an old friend of his, a master of taiji quan. Taiji quan is a form of qigong that is said to have been developed about six hundred years ago as a gentle means of self-defense.

We found the master talking with a group of students. Now in his seventies, he had retired, and one of his students was demonstrating to a small group of young men. Nearby, the master's wife was leading four women in fan dancing. Their colorful fans snapped in rhythm to the playful Chinese music that emanated from a small boom-box sitting on a park bench. Master Wang and his friend greeted each other warmly, and I left them to talk while I wandered through the gardens.

The autumn air, sweet with the delicate fragrance of *Osmanthus* trees, inspired me to focus on the pleasure of its scent. As I walked, I envisioned myself inhaling qi from these tiny blooms, drinking in their sweet nectar like honeyed clouds. I allowed this energy to circulate through me, nourishing each cell of my body, before passing out through my feet. As my arms and body followed the movements of my mind, I was practicing qigong as unselfconsciously as the people around me.

You don't need to be young or physically fit to practice qigong, unless you are practicing the hard, external styles. Nor do you need to begin practicing during childhood to reap meaningful results. If you only have ten minutes to practice each day, that's a start. Thirty minutes is better, and an hour a day is better yet. The length of time you practice at a session, however, is up to you. It is a fabulous experience to practice qigong in nature, as I was doing. Walking forms of qigong are ideal to practice outdoors amid beautiful surroundings. But you can also practice in a closet, if need be, because qigong doesn't require that you walk at all, or even move your feet. Uniquely versatile and adaptable, qigong is truly a practice for all seasons.

QIGONG VERSUS ORDINARY EXERCISE

It was a new experience for me to see so many adults, young and old intermingled, just relaxing outdoors and moving their bodies in play. Some were practicing sword dancing, while others did fan dancing. In the distance, a large crowd practiced ballroom dancing! There were people doing taiji and qigong, as well as people doing calisthenics. With such a diverse array of activity going on around me, I began to ponder the difference between qigong and some of these other forms of exercise.

What distinguishes qigong from ordinary exercise? Exercise works the physical body, but it neither trains the mind nor works directly with the subtle energy of qi. Ordinary exercise can develop your muscles, while your mind remains preoccupied with your next business meeting. Exercise builds physical fitness and strengthens the heart, but it can also stress the body and can deplete a weak body's energy reserves. Qigong, on the other hand, simultaneously engages the mind, body and spirit, and can be used specifically to improve the function of your liver, kidneys and other organs. Because qigong slows oxygen consumption, while delivering more oxygen to the cells, it increases energy reserves rather than depletes them.

Nevertheless, the line between qigong and exercise is sometimes a fine one. Simple forms of qigong, like exercise, rely on body movements and breathing to move the qi where it needs to go. Advanced levels of qigong may rely entirely on moving qi with the mind and can involve gaining voluntary control over blood pressure, heart rate or one's state of consciousness. The rule of thumb is, if you are consciously working with qi, you are doing qigong; if you are unaware of qi, you are exercising. The movements of taiji quan, taiji sword dance and fan dance, for example, are all similar and may be practiced either as qigong or as exercise, depending on the practitioners' awareness of qi and how they engage their minds.

The truth is, the average person can watch someone perform a slow movement and have no way of knowing for sure whether it is true qigong or simply exercise. I sometimes demonstrate this to people by raising my arms slowly as my knees sink, and then lowering my arms as my knees straighten. I do this twice—first as an exercise and then as qigong. Both outer movements look the same. The difference rests in the subjective experience of the practitioner. For me, the first experience is nothing special, while the second one creates a soothing sense of inner fluidity and the sensation of a subtle, tingling wave.

THE DANCE OF YIN AND YANG

When I returned to the center of the garden, I discovered Master Wang and the taiji master playing *push hands*, a form of taiji that involves two participants. Push hands is one of my husband's favorite pastimes, and he misses having skilled partners to practice with at home in Hawaii. As I watched the two masters, it was like watching a moving work of art, a sculpture that was being continually transformed through the subtle interplay of energies passing between them. Although the energy itself was invisible to my eye, their bodies defined its movement in much the same way that supple fronds of seaweed define the surge and retreat of surf. Here before me was a wonderful demonstration of an ancient principle that pervades Chinese culture to this day: the dance of *yin* and *yang*.

In the ancient Chinese worldview, qi is composed of two complementary and interrelated aspects, or polarities, called yin and yang. Yin is the negative polarity, representing aspects that are cool, dark and feminine. Yang is the positive polarity, representing aspects that are hot, light and masculine. Yin and yang are entirely relative to one another and are never static. As one aspect grows, the other recedes in the same motion, like day turning into night or cold warming into hot. Yin is continually transforming into yang, and yang transforms into yin, as both naturally seek dynamic balance and harmony. In Chinese philosophy, it is this ever-changing ebb and flow of yin and yang qualities, dancing around a central point of balance, that drives the universe and all of its systems.

This symbol graphically illustrates the principles of yin and yang. It depicts the circle of life, of nature, the unity of the cosmos, the cycling interrelatedness of all things. Yang (white) and yin (black) are two apparently opposing

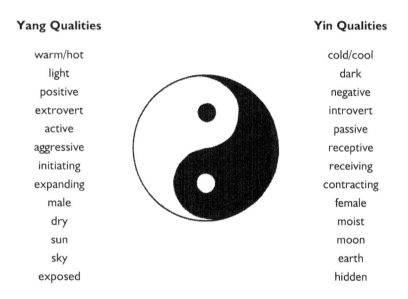

Yang Qualities	Yin Qualities
warm/hot	cold/cool
light	dark
positive	negative
extrovert	introvert
active	passive
aggressive	receptive
initiating	receiving
expanding	contracting
male	female
dry	moist
sun	moon
sky	earth
exposed	hidden

forces that are also interdependent, equal and integrated aspects of one whole. They are defined as much by what they are not as by what they are. The dots signify the essence of each polarity within the heart of the other, indicating that nothing is absolute nor truly opposing, for within each lies the seed of the other.

THE THEORY OF QIGONG

According to traditional Chinese philosophy, the dance of yin and yang fuels the flow of qi, which in turn powers the universe and creates all life. To sustain life, qi must flow. To sustain harmony and health, qi's yin and yang aspects must be in balance with one another.

In a healthy body, the mind is sharp, the body is strong and the immune system is able to defend against germs and mutant cells. When the nourishing flow of qi becomes diminished, weak, restricted or blocked, the body weakens and becomes susceptible to invaders such as viruses and bacteria, or to the development of cancer cells. These principles hold true whether we are speaking of the qi within our body or in nature at large.

Many things can cause qi flow to become restricted and sometimes blocked in parts of the body. It may be physical trauma such as a car accident, a sports injury or even a stubbed toe. It may be emotional trauma such as worry, fear, grief and resentment. It may be tense, tight muscles caused by physical or emotional stress, or even a change in the weather. Whatever the form of stress may be, it shuts down the natural flow of subtle energy, causing discomfort and creating conditions for illness.

If the circulation of qi remains restricted or blocked, excesses and deficiencies of qi develop. In class, Master Wang uses the analogy of a car crash that blocks the flow of traffic. Like a string of cars backed up behind a crash on the highway, qi builds up excessively on the "upstream" side of the blockage and becomes deficient on the "downstream" side. Qi that isn't flowing suffers in quality; it becomes stagnant and foul, like stagnant water in a pond. Without a nourishing flow of fresh qi to sustain them, the affected organs and systems weaken. If not corrected, the energetic imbalance or blockage eventually manifests as disease.

When crashed cars are removed from the highway, traffic can flow easily again. Likewise, when stagnant qi is removed and a full, balanced circulation of qi is restored, healing is naturally initiated. An ancient Chinese aphorism says, "Qi leads the blood." Blood is like a river that brings nutrition to the cells as it carries off wastes. Wherever qi goes, the blood follows. Where there is insufficient qi, the blood is unable to do its work in maintaining a healthy body.

Just as it is qi that leads the blood, it is the mind that leads qi. Our thoughts, and the emotions to which they give rise, influence the physical body through the medium of qi. While negative thoughts and emotions inhibit our health by contracting the body and restricting qi flow, positive thoughts and emotions support good health and well-being by allowing qi to move freely. When our body is relaxed and unafraid, qi can circulate freely and do its work.

We demonstrate an intuitive sense of the relationship between attitude, subtle energy and physiology in slang phrases such as "I'm turned off," "she's tuned in" and "he's really charged up." Body language also makes this relationship evident. In the following diagram, can you identify whose qi flow is more contracted, A or B?

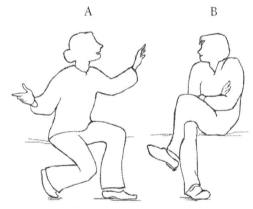

A   B

(Answer: If you said B, you're right.)

PART TWO   WITH ROOTS IN
            ANCIENT CHINA

Grandfather Wang
in 1932

CHAPTER 4

The Power to Heal

Our stay in China offered me a lingering gaze through that proverbial "window on the past," broadening my understanding of qigong's rich history while illuminating qigong's role in my husband's personal past. When we visited Shanghai, my husband showed me the neighborhood where he had lived as a boy. I discovered the important role qigong healing had played in his early childhood.

Qing Chuan Wang (or Wang Qing Chuan, as he is called in China, where it is the custom to place the surname first) was born in 1943 into a prosperous, loving and hard working family. He was a rambunctious and happy child, intense and with an irrepressible spirit. As a small boy, his happiest hours were spent in nature, playing with the bugs, birds and geckos, or "wall tigers," that roamed the yard and shrubbery around his family's French colonial-style house in the heart of Old Shanghai. Active, curious and always generous when it came to others, he loved to bring leftover *fan*, or cooked rice, to feed minnows in the pond at the nearby park and clamber atop anything that could be climbed.

When he was five years old, Qing Chuan Wang's life took a sudden turn. He had been feeling unwell, and one morning he awoke to discover that he couldn't move his right arm. Despite his best efforts, the arm hung limp at his side. He called his mother to show her this disturbing state of affairs. Within the hour, he was rushed to the hospital on foot, carried in the arms of one of his father's employees. At the hospital, the grim diagnosis was polio.

Qing Chuan's father, Zhuang Ming, came from a family of healers and so he knew much about healing. The Wang home was filled with books, many of them old texts on traditional medicine that belonged to Zhuang Ming and his father. However, during the years when Qing Chuan was young, his father had little time to think about healing. He was at the peak of his career as a self-made businessman, supervising international contracts and overseeing a large staff. Besides, he and Qing Chuan's mother, Yung Fong, were forward-thinking people who believed that modern medicine was superior to the old country ways. Qing Chuan's older brother and sister both planned to carry on the family's healing tradition and were already thinking ahead to medical school with the intention of becoming doctors of Chinese *and* Western medicine.

In the 1940s, however, Western medicine was powerless against polio. All eyes turned toward his grandfather.

GRANDFATHER HEALER

Grandfather Wang was accomplished in both qigong healing and the martial arts. In fact, he was well-known throughout the region as a master of the

Wudang style of qigong, a comprehensive school that included healing, spiritual and martial arts. Wudang qigong practices had been passed down through many generations from father to son within the Wang family.

As a young man, Grandfather Wang focused on qigong for self-defense. Those were the last years of the Qing (Manchu) Dynasty, when the government was weak and lawlessness prevailed. Amid political unrest, thieves and revolutionaries roamed the land, sometimes robbing people or, worse yet, murdering them and taking over their homesteads. Men like Grandfather Wang relied on their qigong fighting skills to protect their families. They also competed with one another for sport. Like the famous gunslingers in the American Old West, a master's reputation spread by word of mouth. Grandfather Wang was one of the "top guns" of his day, and qigong masters traveled long distances to his hometown of Wuxi to test their skills against his.

Nevertheless, despite his martial arts victories and considerable healing abilities, life in rural China wasn't easy, and Grandfather Wang dreamed of a better existence for his six children. As they grew, he encouraged his offspring to seek their fortunes in the city. And so it was that Qing Chuan's father settled in Shanghai. He worked his way up through the printing business and, by the time Qing Chuan was born, he owned and operated the largest photo printing company in China.

Qing Chuan sat next to Grandfather Wang as the old man waved his hands in the air along the boy's small arm, crippled with polio. He seemed to be pulling and pushing the air around, as if it were thick as honey. Occasionally, the old man gave a loud and unexpected yell, "Hyaahh!" as he seemed to throw something invisible into Qing Chuan's shoulder. It always made the little boy jump before bursting into giggles of pleasure at the surprise.

Grandfather Wang explained that he was doing "emitted qi" therapy. He worked on the boy's body a little bit every day, patiently running qi back and forth through the damaged nerves and tissues. He was using his own life-force as well as the energies of nature to stimulate the flow of his grandson's qi energy through the paralyzed arm. By doing this repeatedly, he removed the blocked, stagnant energy and encouraged fresh qi to flow. Step by step, every day, the flowing current of fresh qi revitalized the boy's body, helping the nerves to regenerate and the body to heal itself.

ANCIENT ROOTS

For thousands of years, energy practices were handed down within Chinese families and monasteries, with limited or no outside exchange. Kept secret from the masses, these practices became shrouded in mystery and superstition. It has only been in the last century, through efforts by the Chinese government to demystify and regulate qigong, that it has entered the public arena. In fact, the term *qigong* itself only came into popular usage during the twentieth century, uniting various energy practices that have their roots as far back as four thousand years ago. Today these diverse practices are all correctly called *qigong*.

The Chinese have practiced methods of working with qi since ancient times. Scholars believe the earliest forms of qigong probably evolved from shamanic practices and ancient forms of dancing. Chinese shamans performed animal dances to chase away bad energies. They observed how animals made instinctive movements—such as stretching, leaping and methods of breathing—to promote healing, obtain food and resist attack from predators. People adapted these along with their own instinctive forms of movement to regulate physiology and improve health. Animal dances figure prominently throughout qigong's history, and to this day many qigong movements carry animal names.

Since the history of qigong predates the written word, researchers rely on written accounts of earlier times, as well as ancient artifacts such as carvings and drawings, to trace qigong's roots. The most well-known ancient form

of qigong is Dao-yin. *Dao-yin* means "to lead and guide energy." A silk cloth
that was unearthed from a tomb dating back to the third century B.C.E. dis-
plays colored illustrations of human figures in various postures performing
Dao-yin. Captions provide animal names that are believed to be names for the
movements, along with the names of specific ailments (such as hypertension,
knee pain and so on) and directions on how to move the body. Movements
similar to those appearing on the Dao-yin silk are still practiced today as a simple form of qigong.

Some Ancient Forms of Qigong

- Anqiao—*massage*
- Dao-yin—*lead and guide qi*
- Fuqi—*taking in qi*
- Jingzuo—*sitting still*
- Shiqi—*living on qi*
- Shushu—*counting breaths*
- Tuna—*exhalation and inhalation*
- Wogong—*lying down exercises*
- Xingqi—*directing and guiding qi*
- Zuochan—*sitting meditation*

Source: *Chinese Qigong*, Publishing House of Shanghai
College of Traditional Chinese Medicine, p.2

As the above list indicates, ancient people practiced with qi in many
different ways. It was common for a particular family's method to include just

one form of practice, such as a certain breathing technique to strengthen the body's qi, or a particular movement to promote qi flow through the body. In contrast with these simpler forms, Grandfather Wang practiced a higher level of qigong that involved using the mind. His comprehensive knowledge of how to work with qi came from the Wudang tradition and was based on principles of understanding that allowed room for experimentation and creativity, not just rote performance.

FOLLOWING THE DAO

To better understand qigong in general and Grandfather Wang's qigong in particular, we must look at the soil from which it arose. The ancient Chinese were an agrarian society, living close to the land. They saw themselves as part of the vast system of nature that moved in accordance with predictable cycles of change. Trees grow full, spread their seeds, and eventually die. Even mountains rise and fall away. Yet, within this continually changing scene, an innate balance and harmony sustains and supports all life. Between extremes of too much and too little, life abounds. This was the worldview of Daoism, China's grass-roots spiritual, cultural and philosophical tradition.

Of the many historic influences that guided qigong's development, Daoism was the most significant. The Daoists were concerned with matters of practical, everyday life, as well as humanity's relationship to the universe. They perceived that humans and the universe were part of a continuum, powered throughout by the same qi. As without, so within. As above, so below. In this holistic view of life, humanity cannot be separated from nature because people are an expression of nature and must live according to nature's principles.

The Daoist goal is to live a peaceful and happy life, in good health and in harmony with others. The way to accomplish this is to live in accordance with the Dao, the way of nature. Just as the Daoists learned to cultivate healthy crops, they also learned to cultivate health and longevity, following the same balance of yin and yang forces that governed their universe. For example, the *Dao de Jing,* a classic text of Daoist philosophy written by the sage Lao Zi in the fourth century B.C.E., mentions working with qi to achieve the flexibility of a child.

Because the Daoists saw spirit and body as parts of a whole, they valued the equal development of both. In this perspective, the subtle, invisible world of energy, emotions and spirit is every bit as valid and significant as the world's physical components. To try to explain how life works without including the role of its non-physical aspects would be like trying to explain the swaying of palm trees without speaking of wind, or the nature of a shadow without mentioning the sun. Because the spiritual gives birth to the physical and also permeates everyday life, all life is regarded as spiritual and must be cared for and respected accordingly. Not surprisingly, China's traditional approach to healing reflects the holistic integration that characterizes the Daoist worldview.

TRADITIONAL CHINESE MEDICINE

Two of China's great gifts to the world are qigong and traditional Chinese medicine. Medicine and qigong evolved alongside one another, influencing and guiding one another over thousands of years. In fact, qigong healing methods form the foundation of Chinese medicine. Today, the field of qigong that focuses on health and healing is called "medical qigong."

In Grandfather Wang's time, it was common for virtually every family to have some knowledge of the folk healing arts. Acupuncture, qi massage, qigong exercise, herbs and foods were all used to restore and maintain inner balance. Then as well as now, these practices can be considered aspects of both qigong and traditional Chinese medicine.

Traditional Chinese medicine has one simple goal: to promote balanced conditions in which life can thrive. Contrary to the Western approach to disease—focused on attacking and destroying invading organisms and diseased cells—the approach used by traditional Chinese medicine is to strengthen the body's internal environment so that it can better ward off or withstand illness, and self-heal. This is accomplished by manipulating qi in order to bring its yin and yang aspects into balance.

Chinese medicine forms a complex and complete theoretical system. Nevertheless, it can seem as foreign to a Western-trained doctor as, say, a visit to another planet. The reason for this is simple: Western medicine focuses on the physical body while ignoring its bioelectrical nature. Chinese medicine, on the other hand, works exclusively with the body's bioelectrical nature, manipulating it to improve physical health. In the Chinese worldview, qi energy circulates through the body along primary pathways called *meridians,* and is stored throughout the body in channels called *collaterals* and in storage areas called *dan tian.*

The body has three main dan tian: the *lower* dan tian, located in the lower abdomen, the *middle* dan tian, located in the heart area at the center of the chest, and the *upper* dan tian, located in the pituitary region between and behind the eyes. Dan tian are energy centers that serve to generate and store qi, as well as pump qi through the body. We can recharge our dan tian and increase our vitality by practicing qigong exercises. When the term dan tian is used without specifying a location, it refers to the lower dan tian, for this is the body's main energy center. It connects to the front of the body through the navel area, and to the back of the body through the *mingmen*, or "gate of life," located at the small of the back roughly opposite the navel. In qigong and traditional Chinese medicine, the front of the body and the inside of the limbs are referred to as the "yin" side of the body, while the back of the body and outsides of the limbs are called the "yang" side.

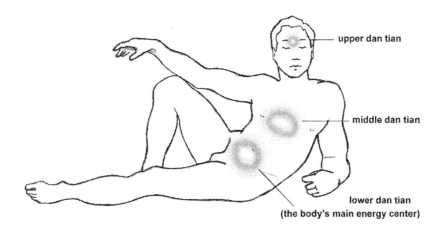

The meridians serve as highways that channel qi along precise routes throughout the body, including six that flow through the arms and fingers, and six through the legs and toes. Each meridian is associated with one of the body's organs, and circulates the energetic qualities of that organ to other parts of the body. Think, for example, of electricity flowing unimpeded through wires, allowing appliances to work properly, or water flowing through pipes all the way from a distant reservoir into your kitchen sink. Collaterals are qi reservoirs. By storing and releasing qi, they help regulate the quantity of qi flowing through the meridians at any given time.

Traditional Chinese medicine regards each organ and its associated meridian as an integrated system, the health of which depends on proper balance of yin and yang, and an adequate supply and circulation of qi. When qi flowing through an organ-system becomes blocked and out of balance, traditional doctors stimulate specific points along the meridians, called acupuncture points, or "acupoints." Acupoints serve to generate, pump, store and release qi into the greater system.

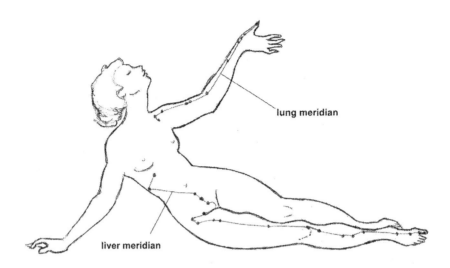

lung meridian

liver meridian

Twelve major meridians are associated with the body's organ systems. Here you see the lung meridian (running from thumb to lung) and liver meridian (running from big toe to liver), along with the main acupoints located along these meridians.

Acupuncturists stimulate acupoints by inserting hair-thin needles into the skin. However, a skilled qigong master capable of directing emitted qi can stimulate acupoints without the use of needles, simply by projecting a stream of force from his fingers directly into the desired point on the body. This method of "acupuncture without needles" is one of the ways Grandfather Wang used qigong to treat Qing Chuan's arm when he had polio.

Grandfather Wang explained that, although using needles is less tiring than using your own qi, qi emitted directly from the fingers has other benefits. It can actually be more powerful and it can be applied to delicate areas, such as near the lungs, where you wouldn't want to poke around with needles. Later on, Grandfather would teach Qing Chuan how to do "acupuncture without needles" on others, but for now, his focus was on helping the boy return to health.

Under his grandfather's expert care, using a combination of herbs, qi massage and emitted qi therapy, Qing Chuan soon regained use of his arm. The healing was so complete that years later, when he was recruited to play professional sports, none of the recruiters guessed his arm had been paralyzed by polio as a child.

CHAPTER 5

Wudang Qigong

When Qing Chuan was six years old—the year the Communists came into power—Grandfather Wang began teaching him qigong. He taught him the Wudang qigong practices that had been passed down through the family over generations.

Wudang qigong is China's most famous lineage of Daoist qigong and represents one of the two main traditions of qigong in China. It is a broad system, containing many forms and styles that are practiced for health, spiritual growth and martial arts. Today these are still the three main arenas of qigong practice.

Qigong is practiced for health:

- to maintain health
- to increase well-being
- to heal disease and injuries
- to balance the emotions
- to increase longevity

for spiritual growth:

- for personal growth
- to facilitate meditation
- to improve concentration
- to experience altered states of consciousness

for martial arts:

- for sports
- for showmanship and entertainment
- for physical fitness
- for self-defense

THE WUDANG LINEAGE

The roots of Wudang qigong trace back to the monasteries of the Wudang Mountains in Hubei province, where it arose from the gentle internal energy arts practiced by Daoist monks.

Legend has it that, six hundred years ago during the Ming dynasty, a Daoist monk became known for his extraordinary abilities. The monk's name was Zhang San-feng, and he came from Wudang Dao Kuan, a monastery in the Wudang Mountains. He spent many years cultivating the Dao and perfecting his martial arts and healing skills, and was able to cure many people of disease. He called his system of qigong "Wudang Longmen," which means "Dragon Gate, from Wudang." Zhang San-feng loved to visit other Daoist monasteries, called *kuans*, scattered throughout the Wudang Mountains. Each monastery had its own style of qigong. However, after encountering Zhang, monks at these monasteries adopted his methods. Gradually, all the kuans in the region came to follow the Wudang Longmen school.

As word of Zhang's greatness continued to spread, he was brought to serve at the emperor's court. Eventually, the name of his system, which combined martial art forms of qigong and more meditative practices, was shortened from Wudang Longmen to Wudang. Zhang San-feng is known as the patriarch of Wudang qigong, as well as the originator of taiji chuan. Although his existence is considered legendary by some, it is a matter of historic record. Scholars debate the accuracy of these early records because, if all of them were true, Zhang San-feng would have lived far beyond a normal lifespan.

LEARNING QIGONG

To the average person in China in the 1940s—as throughout Chinese history—qigong was something mysterious that was practiced within monasteries or individual families. Most people didn't understand qigong, nor were they especially interested in exploring it. There was no formal qigong education in the sense of taking classes or writing down information. There were no books about qigong. Qigong was a sort of secret society, and information was passed verbally through discussion and experience. Qigong masters were sometimes persecuted for their abilities and considered to be demons, sorcerers and wizards.

In those days, as in ancient times, qigong masters often sought one or two exceptional students whom they could train to a high level. When someone sought to learn qigong from a master, he had to earn the privilege. If the master were not a member of the family or monastery, the aspiring student had to bond with him first by acting as his son. A student would follow the master and serve him. He would clean the master's house, run errands for him, bring him food and other thoughtful gifts, and try to anticipate the master's every need. Only after the master began to look upon the would-be student as his son would teaching begin. Although daughters were sometimes taught qigong, more often than not, a master adopted his daughter's husband and trained him instead.

Once the master accepted a student, the bond lasted for life. A student showed the same respect and devotion to his master that he gave to his own parents. Typically, a master would never take more than a few students. Such has been the tradition of qigong. To Westerners, this may sound like needless ritual or superficial formality, but the tradition is rooted in an understanding of energy. All emotions affect the subtle energy field. When a master is looking for a student he can train to a high level, he looks for someone who is smart, disciplined and sensitive to energy. But that's not all. Energy must flow easily between them. This happens most naturally when two people share close friendship, love and understanding.

Qing Chuan was fortunate to have his grandfather close at hand. Qigong practice appealed to young Qing Chuan's intense nature and he was eager to probe its hidden depths. First Grandfather Wang taught him the pose known as "Standing like a Tree" to strengthen and build up the qi. He then introduced the boy to forms of Wudang qigong's hard martial arts. He did so while admonishing his grandson never to compete in that arena, as he himself had done as a youth. "Today you fight others," he would say, "but tomorrow they will fight you. To be at the top is a passing moment; don't waste your time and good health competing with others." Over the years, Grandfather Wang had seen many men crippled and killed as a result of hard qigong practices. He considered himself fortunate to have weathered his youth unscathed and, with time and experience, came to regard soft qigong as superior to hard qigong in all ways. "Soft qigong is like water," he explained. "It is yielding enough to assume whatever form contains it, yet powerful enough to wear away mountains!"

At first, Qing Chuan loved the hard forms of qigong best. In the typical way of boys, he loved the feeling of power and strength that came from these practices. But as his sensitivity to qi increased, he became aware of a deeper, more satisfying experience that came from feeling the qi itself. Grandfather Wang taught young Qing Chuan how to lead qi with his mind, showing him how to combine the power of intention with a quiet but focused inner awareness. Under his grandfather's guidance, Qing Chuan became adept at forms of soft, internal qigong and qi meditation. He learned how to perform *qi tuina* (qi massage) and qi acupuncture, how to administer qi tonics and herbs, and how to emit external qi and use it to help others heal. Over time, Qing Chuan developed and improved on the family methods he learned from his grandfather, creating methods of his own, through his own direct experience of qi.

It was his grandfather who taught Qing Chuan the importance of the three principles he teaches today: *relax*, *open* and *smile*. The qigong smile was Grandfather Wang's trademark. Other qigong masters would typically scowl or have a serious expression to convey a sense of power. As Qing Chuan now explains to his own students, a serious expression is fine for the military, but not for qigong. You must invite the qi like a dear friend, not demand that it bow to your will. The greatest strength is in gentleness; the greatest power is manifest through the willing attraction of the heart.

QIGONG UNDER COMMUNISM

During the early years of Communism, the government was very interested in providing healthcare for the masses. They began to study qigong in an effort to systematize it, weed out the genuine from the false, develop new training methods and examine qigong's role in healing. The first qigong sanatorium was established in 1955, followed in quick succession by the initiation of qigong classes to train health practitioners and the establishment of a second qigong sanatorium. In 1959, China held the first national conference on qigong, with representatives from seventeen provinces in attendance.

For the first time in history, qigong was moving out from behind its traditionally closed doors. With government endorsement, the general public was introduced to simple forms of qigong for health and healing. Parks and gardens became filled with people practicing qigong. It was probably not unlike the scenes I witnessed in the parks on my first visit to Shanghai.

FROM BASKETBALL TO ACCOUNTING

When Qing Chuan was fifteen, he was recruited by the government to play professional basketball. He was tall and loved sports. Thanks to his qigong training, he was also centered and fast on his feet. He enrolled at the Shanghai School of Sports, where China's most skilled athletes train for the Olympics. The school became Qing Chuan's home for the next few years. He followed a rigorous schedule during the week, but was allowed to return home on week- ends to visit his parents and grandfather, who was now well advanced in years.

By the following spring, a famine was sweeping across China. Its three-year tour of devastation left some thirty million people dead. Most of those who did not starve to death had to struggle to find food. Because they were top athletes in training, Qing Chuan and his fellow students at the School of Sports were among the fortunate few who remained well fed during this dark period of China's history.

At the School of Sports, Qing Chuan met Master Cai Hong Qiang, China's leading coach of Shaolin gong fu, the most famous Buddhist lineage of qigong. Master Cai was assigned to be Qing Chuan's personal trainer. For an hour each day, Master Cai trained Qing Chuan in gong fu arts, while the other boys did group exercises. Under Master Cai's tutelage, Qing Chuan not only became adept at dunking a basket, but learned skills that would further his future career as a teacher of energy arts.

In 1962, less than a year after the famine had passed, Qing Chuan developed a knee injury. Unable to rest his knee sufficiently due to a strict and demanding schedule, the injury gradually became more serious. His doctors wanted to operate on the knee, but they could not guarantee a full recovery. As Qing Chuan weighed the odds, it seemed to him that he had only about a fifty-fifty chance of walking normally again if he went ahead with surgery. Rather than gamble on such poor odds for complete recovery, he decided against the operation.

Just nineteen years old, Qing Chuan left basketball. Unable to either stand or sit for more than five or ten minutes at a time without excruciating pain, he enrolled in school to become a certified public accountant. Here, at least, was a desk job he could do sitting down.

For the second time, it was qigong that turned Qing Chuan's life around. With his grandfather's encouragement, Qing Chuan decided to heal his knee by himself. He cut off the cast doctors had placed around it and began treating it using traditional Wudang qigong methods passed down by his grand-father, as well as his own intuition. In every spare moment he worked on his knee, removing the build-up of stale qi and guiding new qi to flow through the injured site. The pain was quickly relieved, and within about three months he was walking normally again. The inspiration to self-heal with the use of qigong was Grandfather's final gift to his grandson, for he died not long thereafter.

Unlike in the U.S., all Chinese schools and universities have manda-tory physical education programs that include sports, martial arts and, more recently, simple forms of qigong. Soon Qing Chuan was playing sports again, but this time as a student in physical education classes while he worked toward his CPA degree at the Shanghai School of Commercial Accounting. Although just a student, his ability and training surpassed that of the instructor, a point the school's directorship didn't fail to notice. Once again, the stars were with Qing Chuan. Just as China erupted in political turmoil in 1966, he completed his training and became employed as a CPA.

WORKING WITH QI

During the bloody first years of the Cultural Revolution, Chairman Mao Zedong banned all large gatherings where people could possibly meet and plot against his political interests. For the better part of a decade, all movies were banned, as were dancing and qigong. Schools and universities were shut down—including the Shanghai School of Sports and the School of Commercial Accounting from which Qing Chuan had just graduated. Many qigong masters were imprisoned for their abilities, and once again, qigong disappeared from public view.

When educational institutions finally began to reopen in the 1970s, Qing Chuan was invited to return to the CPA school where he had been a student, but this time as the school's instructor of athletics, martial arts, taiji and qigong. Sitting at a desk all day, fingers flying along the beads of an abacus, Qing Chuan considered himself fortunate to have stable, productive work during such volatile times. Nevertheless, his heart was not in accounting. He welcomed this opportunity for a teaching career and relished the chance to share his love of qigong and related arts with others. Before long he was teaching martial arts, taiji and qigong at several institutions, as well as qi massage and acupuncture.

As the political environment continued to stabilize, new laws emerged. When a new regulation mandated that all teachers at the college level or above must be certified, Qing Chuan was sent to college to obtain his teaching degree.

He was enrolled at the Shanghai College of Education. In one of those quirks that was characteristic of the times, he continued to teach college graduates and professionals, even as he pursued the certificate that would allow him to legally teach them.

Fellow teachers, students and friends, having witnessed how quickly Qing Chuan had healed his own knee, began coming to him with their health problems, seeking relief from a variety of injuries and illnesses. One of his first sessions was with a co-worker who had suffered from severe chronic headaches for many years. She was sometimes absent from work because of them, and each headache required at least a week for recovery. But after just three sessions of qi therapy from Qing Chuan, her headaches never returned.

Now that qigong was once again sanctioned by the government, people began to seek out Qing Chuan's assistance freely and openly. His students at school addressed him as *laoshi*, or teacher. But beyond school doors, people who came for qigong training or healing called him *sifu*, a Chinese title of respect that means both teacher and master.

Master Xirong Pei on the cover of his book, The Authentic Shaolin and Wudang Gong Fu

Master Qing Chuan Wang with Master Pei in 1990

CHAPTER 6

Grandmaster and Healer

Knowledge of Master Wang's healing ability spread by word of mouth. The people who came to see him were usually local, but some came from far away. One of those was Mr. Ho, a man with chronic lumbago, a rheumatic pain affecting the muscles of the lower back. Mr. Ho had been afflicted with this problem for many years and had traveled to Shanghai, Suzhou and Ningbo, searching in vain for a doctor who could help him. He had tried acupuncture, massage and various ointments and medications, but nothing improved his condition. By the time he arrived at Master Wang's door, he was without much hope. Despite his doubts, he felt very comfortable after the first session, so he returned the following week for another treatment. After two months, much to his surprise, his back was vastly improved. After four months he was completely cured.

DRAMATIC HEALINGS

Using emitted qi therapy, Master Wang successfully treated a wide range of complaints from sprains and sports injuries to digestive problems, colds and arthritis. But greater challenges were in store. One day a professor at the Shanghai College of Traditional Chinese Medicine contacted Master Wang about an ailing relative. The professor's father-in-law, in his sixties, had suffered a stroke. He was paralyzed and unable to lift a finger to look after himself, so the family members had to care for him in turns.

Master Wang was taken to the professor's home to see if he could help his father-in-law. As Master Wang moved his hands gently through the air near the man's body, his sensitive fingers and palms appraised the extent of blockage to the man's qi flow caused by damaged nerves. Then he set to work, coaxing the qi to reestablish a healthy flow.

After the first qi treatment, Master Wang turned to the professor and said, "Now your father-in-law can comb his own hair."

One of the children quickly fetched a comb, and to everyone's delight, the man did exactly that. Amazed and encouraged by his father-in-law's remarkable progress in just one session, the professor asked when he could schedule a second session.

"The qi I have given him will continue to help him over the next few days. I will return in three days for a second session," Master Wang explained.

The second treatment was similar to the first. When it was over, Master Wang said, "Now you can help your father-in-law get up and walk."

The professor looked astonished, but did as Master Wang asked. As the family watched in wonder, the father-in-law rose and accompanied him, step by step, across the room.

The professor's report of this seemingly miraculous healing caused a stir at the Shanghai College of Traditional Chinese Medicine. With the Cultural Revolution still fresh in their memory, doctors did not yet feel safe enough to accept qigong into their medical repertoire, but things were gradually changing. And they did not forget about Master Wang's dramatic demonstration of healing.

QIGONG COMES OF AGE

The end of the Cultural Revolution heralded a period of unprecedented government support for qigong. The leaders of the Communist Party, young revolutionaries during the 1950s, had aged. Previously they had been interested mainly in fighting forms of qigong. Now, thirty years later, they were more concerned with health issues than with waging new battles. Under their sponsorship, official qigong associations and research programs mushroomed. Hundreds of qigong styles made their public debut. Western-trained doctors in modern hospitals continued to explore qigong's potential as a scientifically valid tool of modern medicine. Toward this end, three major institutions—the Shanghai College of Traditional Chinese Medicine, the Shanghai Traditional Medical Research Institute and the Atomic Nucleus Research Institute of the Chinese Academy of Sciences—began working together, using modern scientific instruments to test qi emitted by qigong masters.

THE TEST OF FEN JIU

One day, a man from the Shanghai College of Traditional Chinese Medicine contacted Master Wang. He wanted to know if Master Wang would participate in some scientific tests being conducted at the college. Research money had

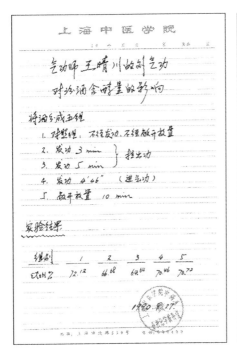
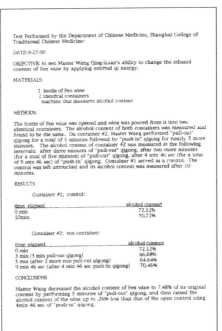

been allocated to study the effects of qi emitted by qigong masters. The scientists wanted to determine if Master Wang could influence inanimate matter by applying external qi. The material to be tested was *fen jiu*, China's most potent alcoholic beverage. Master Wang's task was to see if he could raise and lower its alcohol content.

Happy to do what he could to help science understand the mysterious workings of qi, Master Wang agreed.

As Master Wang was ushered into the testing room, he was greeted by nearly a dozen researchers and professors who had assembled to observe the test. First, a single bottle of fen jiu was opened, and its contents were poured into two identical containers. Container #1 served as a control and was left untouched. Container #2 was the sample Master Wang was to work on with his qi.

The containers were measured at the beginning of the experiment and the alcohol content in both was found to be 72.12%. Master Wang was asked to try to lower the alcohol content in container #2. The experiment was to last ten minutes.

He focused his full attention on the sample before him and started performing "pull-out" qigong, pulling at the air near the container, while visualizing that he was removing "alcohol qi" and holding the unwavering expectation that alcohol qi was leaving the container.

At the end of three minutes, the alcohol content in container #2 was measured. It had dropped from its initial level of 72.12% to 66.68%. Master Wang continued with "pull-out" qigong for another two minutes, at which time the researcher again measured the alcohol content. It was now down to 64.64%.

Impressed by this rapid 7.48% drop in alcohol, the scientists now instructed him to attempt to *raise* the alcohol content in container #2.

Master Wang began using the force of his intention and emitted qi to push "alcohol qi" back into the fen jiu. After close to five minutes of this "push-in" qigong, the alcohol level in container #2 was measured for the third time. This time the alcohol content had risen from 64.64% to 70.46%.

At this point, the alcohol content of container #1, the untouched control, was measured and found to be 70.72%. The fen jiu in this container, sitting open to air for ten minutes, had lost a small amount of alcohol naturally into the air. Master Wang, after lowering the alcohol in the test container by 7.48% in five minutes, had within five more minutes raised the alcohol content in that container back up to a mere 0.26% less than the alcohol content of the control. In the presence of this group of professors and scientists, he had demonstrated his ability to manipulate inanimate matter without touch, using only his power to control external qi.

17TH AND 18TH PATRIARCHS

During the early years following the Cultural Revolution, Master Wang exchanged knowledge with various other masters of qigong and taiji. He developed close friendships with two Daoist masters. One was a master of painting, calligraphy and Yang style taiji, the other was a master of Wu style taiji. Through the close bond of friendship and mutual respect he developed with these two men, Master Wang broadened his understanding of the Daoist arts and refined his skills in taiji quan and taiji push hands.

One day, a friend came to Master Wang's house with a message. "It's from Grandmaster Xirong Pei, 17th generation patriarch of Wudang qigong," the friend said. "Grandmaster Pei knows of your grandfather's reputation as a skilled master of Wudang qigong. He's heard that your qi is very strong. He wants to feel your qi and see what you can do."

They met at a restaurant for lunch and later returned to Grandmaster Pei's house to talk. Being of the older generation, like Grandfather Wang, Grandmaster Pei had focused on the martial arts because at the time those skills were needed for defense. Yet in true Wudang tradition, he was also a gifted healer, experienced in the spiritual and medical aspects of qigong. Although the historic way of training was for a master to take on only one or two students, in this modern era, his task was to help guide qigong's entry into public awareness by teaching groups. Since the government was distrustful of all things spiritual, his mission was to spread knowledge and basic training of the practical medical and martial aspects of Wudang qigong.

Grandmaster Pei was a kindly and modest man. He and his wife, a qigong master and healer in her own right, were both devoted to helping others and furthering public knowledge and understanding of the qigong arts.

Now getting on in years, Grandmaster Pei recognized in young Master Wang the makings of a worthy and gifted successor who could help spread awareness of Wudang qigong to the next generation. The two men began sharing time together, building friendship and exchanging qigong knowledge and skills. In 1980, five years after their first meeting, Grandmaster Pei appointed Master Wang as his successor, the 18th patriarch of Wudang qigong.

REGULATING QIGONG

In alliance with Grandmaster Pei and the Wudang school of qigong, Master Wang began teaching qigong at Shanghai's leading universities and businesses. Groups of Japanese visitors came from abroad to receive his qigong training and qi therapy at Shanghai's elegant Garden Hotel. As the difficult years of the Cultural Revolution began to recede, medical qigong came into use as an adjunct to standard medical treatment in China's hospitals. Two new hospitals opened that were devoted exclusively to medical qigong. Master Wang began to assist medical doctors with their cases in Shanghai's main hospitals, and taught qigong massage at the Shanghai Zhabei School of Chinese Medicine.

Qigong's growing popularity brought certain challenges. Because historically qigong had been mysterious, even frightening to some, it was relatively easy for skilled imposters to pose as masters and trick the public. The Chinese have always loved to watch and to perform magic. As a result, many people knew how to create illusions and pass them off as feats of qigong. Some masters of qigong are said to move objects without touching them, crush china with their bare hands and cause items to cook or burst into flames. Some are able to leave a small amount of life force within the body after death so it doesn't decay. These phenomena can be genuine and many true cases have been documented, but they are also an opportunity for charlatanism.

For example, chips of white cuttlefish bone may be secretly placed within a china vase. When the vase is smashed, the cuttlefish chips can be easily crushed in the fingers instead of real china. Or two chemicals may be released as a newspaper is crumpled or a towel is twisted, thus setting off a reaction that can generate enough heat to cause steam or flames. Some deceitful practitioners generate "currents of qi" by implanting magnets under the skin of their palms. In such cases, feats attributed to qi are actually a matter of skillful technique.

To sort fact from fiction through careful research, inspection and regulation was a major task the Chinese government undertook wholeheartedly. In 1981, the government established the China Qigong Scientific Research Society, a national organization to oversee qigong regulation and systematization throughout China. Grandmaster Xirong Pei was appointed its Vice President. Vice President was—and still is—the highest office a qigong master can hold because the president of every organization must be a member of the Communist Party.

Master Wang served as council member and director of the Shanghai Wudang Qigong Research Association, and acted as senior consultant to other qigong research organizations, yet he tried to keep a low profile in government affairs. Administering to members of the Party meant curtailed freedom, and he hoped some day to be able to travel abroad.

As part of its ongoing effort to regulate qigong, the government passed a new law requiring all qigong masters to be licensed in order to teach qigong. In 1991, Master Wang was one of 210 participants to pass China's first official qigong licensing review. Licensed as a Senior Qigong Master, Master Wang continued his teaching. Working alongside Grandmaster Pei, he also began training qigong masters to teach. "Grandmaster" is the title for one who teaches teachers—Xirong Pei had been a grandmaster for years, and now Qing Chuan Wang was a grandmaster himself.

ARRIVAL IN A NEW LAND

It was during this time that a taiji master on the Hawaiian island of Kauai contacted a friend of his in Shanghai with a special request: "Find a top qigong master I can bring to America. I have the government contacts needed to sponsor him, and these Westerners need to be exposed to qigong."

By now, Master Wang was recognized as one of China's leading qigong masters. His name was passed to the taiji master on Kauai, and the ball was set in motion.

When Master Wang received the invitation to go to America, he recognized the opportunity for travel about which he had dreamed. The timing was right. With surprising ease, Master Wang received government approval for the journey. Dejun Zhang, head of the highest office of qigong management in the region, was inspired to write Master Wang a personal letter of introduction, endorsement and high praise. Mr. Zhang personally delivered the letter to the American consulate in Shanghai and verbally expressed his hope that the American government and people would soon come to understand the special gifts of qigong.

With approval from the highest level, all other necessary permissions for travel were speedily granted. Soon Master Wang was on his way to a new land. He didn't realize at the time that he was also on his way to a new life.

RECOMMENDATION

Qingchuan Wang, Chinese eminent Chikung master, come from Wuxi, Jiangsu province, is the successor of the 18th generation of Chinese Wutang Longmen school. Wang loved Chikung when he was a boy. Followed his grandfather, he practised Chikung massage, Chikung stimulate acupoint, Chikung acupuncture treatment to cure patient, The methods were handed down in the family from generation to generation. Later, he studied Chikung followed eminent Chikung master Xirong Fei who is the successor of the 17th generation of Chinese Wutang Longmen school. From then on, Wang devoted himself to study Wutang Chikung and master the secrets of it. Now, Wang is the director of the Shanghai Wutang Chikung Association; Senior Chikung doctor of Five-Thunder Palm Recovery Research Academy of Chinese Wutang Chikung; Consultant of folk Chikung massage, Acupuncture and moxibustion Association of Shanghai.

Wang received the first batch of 'Chikung Teaching Certificate in Shanghai' issued by Physical Culture and sports Commission of Shanghai, Wang commands high energy, when he teaches Chikung, he releases energy to his student to help them to be healthier, numbers of patients get better and recovery after practising Wutang Chikung. Some chronic disease sufferers get recovery step by step through Wang's Chikung therapy.

Wang often goes to universities to direct Chikung activity in campus, also, a great number of foreign guests, who lived in first-class hotels such as Hilton Hotel, Garden Hotel etc., mentioned Wang's name to invite him to go the hotel for academic exchanges and some of them beg him for Chikung massage. Therefore, Wang commands high respect and warm welcome by people at home and abroad, in the meanwhile, he wins high appraise!

Now, Master Qingchuan Wang is further probing the secrets of Chikung and how to exploit the powerful energy which exists in the internal of everybody and doing his best to make greater contribution to the health and longevity of mankind.

Chikung Recovery Management Office of Shanghai

Signature

Apr. 26. 1992

INTERNATIONAL WUDANG QIGONG ASSOCIATION.

I, Dejun Zhang, am the head of Shanghai Chikung Recovery Management Office. Shanghai Chikung Recovery Management Office is an administrative department of Shanghai Physical Culture and Sports Commission of the People's Government of Shanghai. This Office is the highest organization of Chikung management in the Shanghai erea.

(BRIEF INTRODUCTION OF MR. QINGCHUAN WANG), which is written personally by myself, is to help the American Government to understand furthermore Mr. Qingchuan Wang.

Thank you.

Signature: _Zhang Dejun_

Date: March 24, 1993

Before me, _Virginia K. Polson_ , Para Consul of the United States of America at Shanghai, appeared _Zhang Dejun_ on _March 24, 1993_ , and signed this document.

VIRGINIA K. POLSON
PARA CONSULAR

71

PART THREE

WELCOME TO
SHING-LING-MEI

CHAPTER 7

Shing-Ling-Mei:
Beautiful Heart, Beautiful Spirit

Under the auspices of his Hawaiian taiji host, Master Wang began giving public demonstrations of qigong, teaching classes, and conducting healing sessions, first on Kauai and later on the island of Oahu. One of the remarkable things about Master Wang was that, even without English language skills, he was able to demonstrate the power of qigong energy to others. He would do this just through the energy he emitted and through his peaceful state. People were astonished to feel the sensations of subtle energy flowing from his fingers as he moved them in the air above their bodies during therapy sessions, and amazed by the inner peace they felt afterwards. With his reputation spreading by word of mouth only, Master Wang soon established a busy practice in Honolulu.

During his first years in the West, Master Wang focused on teaching students how to circulate qi through the body, exchange qi with nature, bring in new qi and flush out the old. He called his style "Long-life qigong" (zhang shou) and focused on teaching students how to control the qi so they could help their bodies heal, improve their health and well-being, and promote longevity.

As Master Wang's command of English improved and as he became more familiar with his students' culture and learning styles, his teaching methods evolved. Drawing from his broad knowledge and experience, he selected those teachings and practices he considered essential for our times. He called this method Shing-ling-mei, which literally translated means heart-spirit-beautiful.

In the Daoist view, all aspects of life are interconnected and interdependent. Your physical health cannot be separated from your emotional and spiritual well-being, or from the relationship you have with your physical surroundings and life-circumstances. Only when balance exists throughout all these aspects of life can an optimal level of health truly prevail. Of the many factors contributing to this balance, Master Wang believes the heart and emotions are most important. By naming his practice Shing-ling-mei, he reminds us of the important role heart and spirit play in transforming ourselves and our world.

As we practice Shing-ling-mei, we work simultaneously on levels that include the physical and non-physical, the seen and unseen. Shing-ling-mei, like other forms of qigong, integrates and harmonizes the body, mind and spirit by implementing three basic principles: regulation of the mind and heart (diao xin), regulation of breath (diao xi), and regulation of posture and alignment (diao shen ti zi shi). When worked on simultaneously, these three regulations combine to form a gestalt that is greater than the sum of its parts.

REGULATION OF MIND AND HEART

The Chinese use one word, *xin*, to mean both mind and heart. While we in the West attribute thoughts to our mind and emotions to our heart, we also recognize that thoughts and emotions go hand-in-hand. Our thoughts spin stories of words and pictures, while our emotions provide the music. A single process is at work—an energetic process—directed by the mind.

Without our conscious direction, thoughts and emotions are like a rudderless ship moving and turning in response to the waves of life, sometimes with unpleasant consequences. Through qigong training, however, the mind's ability to regulate unwanted thoughts and their accompanying emotions is gradually strengthened. In this way, Shing-ling-mei qigong forms a powerful tool for managing emotions as well as health.

Shing-ling-mei trains us to lead qi with the mind. As we learn to do this, we develop the following abilities: We improve our capacity to focus and maintain our attention, as well as to concentrate and direct our intention. We develop the ability of inner visualization (seeing with our mind's eye) and our sense of kinesthesia (feeling the body from within). These abilities strengthen gradually, and it is important not to work the mind too forcefully or intensely in an effort to achieve results. To practice qigong correctly, the mind must focus gently, in a relaxed manner and without force. It's like catching a feather drifting on the breeze—if you lunge at it too forcefully, you push the feather out of reach. Only when you approach softly and easily, without disturbing the surrounding air, can you succeed in catching the feather.

Finding the right degree of focus and concentration takes practice and patience. The beginning student needs to experiment to discover how much concentration is the right amount. If concentration is insufficient, your mind will be distracted continually by passing thoughts and you won't achieve results. If concentration is too strong, you will end up with an uncomfortable feeling of fullness in the head, a headache or other stressful feelings. The correct amount of concentration varies at different times, depending on the number of distracting thoughts with which you must contend.

Qi is such a subtle energy that, to practice qigong of any kind, you must be mentally and emotionally quiet. The main challenge many beginning qigong practitioners face is to free the mind of distracting or disturbing thoughts so the emotions can become calm, and awareness can be relaxed, present and sufficiently focused to begin. To relax and calm your mind and emotions before you begin practice, you can recall pleasant times or relaxing scenes, play soft music, massage your feet or do breathing exercises. Do whatever works best for you. Over time, you will find that as you assume your pose to commence qigong practice, your mind will automatically calm and your attention will focus.

One of the beauties of Shing-ling-mei is that it uses physical pleasure to help regulate the mind and heart. Here's how it works. Suppose worrisome thoughts are making you anxious. As you quiet your mind to begin qigong, your body remains tense because those thoughts are hovering like clouds, just waiting to reclaim your full attention. Once you start qigong practice, you focus on the qi, which draws the mind away from those thoughts and into the energy. As the qi flow begins to expand and harmonize the body, you reconnect with a pool of calming energy that physically soothes you like the warmth of sunshine on a cloudy day. As this happens, you naturally shift into a lighthearted state. It's as if the sun is spreading its warmth throughout your being, dissipating the clouds and leaving comfort in its wake. The more you practice qigong, the more powerful the sensation of qi becomes. Eventually you can learn to shift your state at will and call up what you require in the moment, whether it be feelings of upliftment, inspiration or a winning spirit in sports.

REGULATION OF BREATH

Most qigong styles, including medical qigong, rely on the physical breath to move qi. Yet qi also moves independently of our physical breath, and while we can use our breath to guide it, we don't need to. When Master Wang teaches us about breathing, most of the time he's not talking about the physical breath at all; he's referring to the subtle breath, or *qi breathing*.

Unlike normal breathing, qi breathing is guided by the mind. It focuses on absorbing qi from nature and conducting qi through our body, regardless of what our lungs are doing. This allows us to practice a qigong movement as slowly and deeply as we want, without having to worry about our lungs running out of air. In qi breathing, "inhale" means to bring qi into the body, but "exhale" doesn't mean to send it out of the body—it means to allow qi to flow *through* the body. In addition, we "inhale" as we gently draw qi upward within the body and "exhale" as we lead it down.

In Shing-ling-mei, we use several methods of regulating the breath, ranging from the physical to the more subtle.

Natural respiration refers to normal, physical breathing through the nose. During qigong practice, natural breathing becomes slower, steadier, quieter, finer, deeper and more drawn out. When we are relaxed, it is the abdomen rather than the chest that most naturally moves in and out with our breath. This relaxed form of natural respiration is sometimes called *abdominal breathing*.

By breathing through the nose in a steady, relaxed fashion, we trigger an array of beneficial physiological changes. We slow our heart rate, improve blood flow, calm the brain, trigger changes in enzyme and hormone balance, and decrease energy consumption while delivering more oxygen to the cells.

Dan tian breathing is a form of qi breathing in which we use the mind to guide qi to this important area to facilitate its work. Dan tian breathing is sometimes called *navel breathing* for the sake of simplicity because both are located in the same region. When we were developing embryos within our mother's womb, the exchange of blood, guided by qi, was carried out through our umbilical cord. Beginning qigong students can easily identify their navel, while the dan tian may seem more obscure.

When I was a child, my sister and I would march around the yard chanting, "out goes the bad air, in comes the good," over and over as we inhaled and exhaled deeply. I don't remember where we first heard that phrase, but the Chinese have a similar saying, "cast out the stale, take in the fresh." The process of exchanging stale for fresh is virtually synonymous with the process of life and happens right down to the cellular level. *Whole body breathing,* also called *cellular breathing,* involves exchanging fresh qi for stale throughout the whole body. As we practice in class, Master Wang joyfully tells us to inhale qi through every pore!

REGULATION OF BODY POSTURE

Shing-ling-mei can be practiced standing, sitting or even lying down. By keeping the correct posture during practice, the body is able to relax more deeply, maintain inner quiet and help qi flow more effectively. Moving the body incorrectly—by locking the joints or tensing the muscles, for instance—can inhibit qi flow, as well as cause discomfort that can disturb the quiet mind.

Using a combination of slow, relaxed movements and quiet, focused attention, students learn methods that ultimately allow them to practice qigong powerfully and effectively without moving the physical body at all. For someone who is injured or ill, this is an invaluable healing tool! Even for those in good health, the ability to practice qigong without needing to move the body has unlimited applications. Whether flying on an airplane, riding the bus or sitting in the waiting room at the doctor's office, you can practice qigong discretely.

When I find myself waiting in a long line, instead of feeling restless, I relax my mind, circulate qi through my body, and find the time passing quickly.

Many styles of qigong rely on specific body movements and postures to guide the qi, rather than guiding qi with the mind. For example, medical qigong generally relies on stimulating precise acupuncture points to guide qi along specific meridians, while using different body postures to assist with localized qi flow. Most students are relieved to find out they don't need to know the acupuncture points or meridian pathways to practice Shing-ling-mei.

Specific postures and movements designed to move qi can be especially helpful when teaching and treating large groups of people. After all, not everyone in a group has the same ability to relax and focus the mind, and learning a mental discipline is more difficult than following an outer movement. Yet, as Master Wang explains, reliance on an outer movement to get you to your destination is like being a passenger rather than the driver of a car. Only the driver controls his own route, his destination and the distance he can travel.

A wonderful aspect of Shing-ling-mei is that a novice and an advanced student can practice the same form side-by-side, as each works his or her "edge." This is because the difference lies not in the outer movement, but in what each student does with his or her mind. The novice may be working to guide a single wave of qi through the body without becoming distracted by stray thoughts, while the advanced student may be working to guide qi along several pathways simultaneously to achieve one orchestrated effect. Nevertheless, both share the same experience of challenge, discipline and success, as they each work to expand their limits.

In Shing-ling-mei, the same basic body movement also has the potential to contain many nuances of posture, depending on the level at which one is practicing. Master Wang compares this to writing. First you learn to write simple letters, then gradually you advance to calligraphy. Beautiful calligraphy isn't necessary for effective results, yet it is one avenue of mastery and one of the many pleasures of the practice.

In most qigong practices, students learn a specific "form," or sequence of body postures, that never changes. Yet in Shing-ling-mei, this is not always the case. Learning a number of fixed movements can be beneficial when you are just starting Shing-ling-mei. (The ones in this book, for instance, provide a firm foundation for understanding the principles of mind and movement, and for establishing a practice at home.) Nevertheless, Master Wang emphasizes that qigong is ultimately about learning energy management, not about mastering an outer form.

Master Wang allows his qigong movements to gradually change over time, so the practice remains fresh and alive. In class, he introduces movements he finds especially powerful and effective. He frequently modifies them according to what he feels his students can handle at any given time. This evolution of movement creates a spirit of creativity and non-attachment to "having to know it all." One of Master Wang's students used to complain that the movements in class were always changing. She was accustomed to excelling in whatever she did, and felt these changes prevented her from committing the steps to memory as quickly as possible. She complained at almost every class, and I began to wonder why she kept coming. Then one day, her attitude completely shifted. She pulled me aside after class and enthusiastically shared her insight with me. "Now I see this practice as a living, evolving art that can only be fresh in the moment if Master Wang allows it to breathe and grow, like a plant. He's letting the movement transform itself, like the ever-changing Dao!" She never complained again.

TENDING THE SPIRIT

While many people use Shing-ling-mei simply as a tool for relaxation, it also offers a means of getting in touch with our inner spiritual nature and the source of our creativity. Many of us are so outwardly focused during the course of daily life that we rarely pause to still our thoughts and turn within. However, we can learn to do this through qigong.

Shing-ling-mei, like other forms of qigong, includes both moving and still forms of meditation. It is especially valuable for people who want to meditate but find it difficult to silence the thinking mind. Giving our attention something pleasurable to focus on—the sensation of qi—allows the mind to gently disengage from its stream of thoughts and naturally gravitate toward a silent state.

Virtually all great spiritual traditions include some form of meditation. In China, qigong was traditionally viewed as one of the key pathways for spiritual development because, through its meditative practice, one can arrive at a nonverbal understanding of life's mysteries—not an intellectual analysis, but an intuitive knowing that speaks louder than words. Through meditation we find relief from the outer world of nagging needs, feelings of incompleteness, worry and perpetual seeking. Gradually, we come to realize that all these disturbed feelings arise from our own thinking—the stories we play out in our mind, the fearful projections we have of the future—and the consequent contraction this causes on our flow of life-force energy. By relaxing the mind and releasing these contractions, thereby allowing life force to flow fully, disturbances of the mind disappear and, along with them, all negativity vanishes as well. What is left is the blissful experience of wholeness, completeness and unbounded awareness. This is not just theory, but something anyone with sufficient commitment and dedication can test for himself or herself.

The first time I got an inkling of what this was like, I was practicing qigong at my home on Kauai in a light, airy room overlooking the sea. With the help of a beautiful setting and a contented, open-hearted frame of mind, I was intent merely on appreciating my connection with the universe around me. I circulated qi through my body and exchanged it with the surrounding qi in wonderfully circular, continuous flowing motions. In a happy, thought-free state, I focused gently on the qi flow. As it typically does during practice, the qi sensation gradually strengthened and as I closed my eyes I began to feel more aware of the flowing qi than of my physical body. The qi felt like a current of some exquisitely soft and wonderful vibration. I felt saturated with oxygen, like the feeling of not needing to breathe that immediately follows a deep, relaxing sigh. As I became increasingly absorbed in the qi, I began to feel like aliveness itself, a field of awareness that was vibrant, unlimited, everywhere. I was aware of my body moving, yet it was as light and thin as a cellophane wrapper, moving within my own vast embrace.

What I had just experienced is known as entering the *qi state*. The qi state is one of the more striking aspects of qigong. It is a state in which we can transcend our limited experience of self. We can do this by tuning into the life-force energy that pervades and sustains the universe—the same qi that pervades and animates our body. We are aware because of qi, and we can also use qi to extend our awareness beyond the boundaries of our body.

In qigong class, Master Wang sometimes invites us to contemplate the nature of our sense of self. Our sense of self is usually limited, and also more arbitrary than we may realize. It may include just our mind and body, or may include our family or some group to which we belong. In other words, our personal sense of self becomes whatever our mind and emotions identify with at the moment. Qigong can help us experience a sense of self beyond this personal "I." When we enter what's called the "qi state," boundaries of separation fall away as we perceive a greater sense of "Self."

Developing the Spirit

The Chinese call spiritual energy *shen*. Shen is the energy of our consciousness. It is a form of qi that is used throughout all levels of our practice. Our body naturally produces spiritual energy as one of the three main forms of qi that it needs to function. In very simple terms, we can think of *jing*, *qi* and *shen* as three levels of energy refinement, each increasingly subtle. *Jing* is associated with water and forms the basic building blocks of life, such as food, blood and sexual fluids. *Qi* is associated with air and is the energy that burns our fuel and runs our metabolism. *Shen* is associated with light and is the energy of consciousness and spirit. *Jing*, *qi* and *shen* must exist in balance with one another for good health and well-being to prevail.

In spiritual traditions that focus primarily on developing shen, practitioners must take care to balance the development of their spiritual energy with some form of physical exercise, or they risk encountering weakness and illness in the physical body. This is because the body has only so much life energy with which to work. *Jing* and *qi* are used to run the body and are stored within the body. An excess supply of *jing* and *qi* can be converted to *shen* without stealing from the body's needs. If spiritual practices convert *jing* and *qi* into *shen* when the body doesn't have a sufficient supply of the former for its needs, *jing* and *qi* will become deficient. It is like constructing a tall building. What happens if you work on the upper levels of a building before an adequate foundation has been laid? The building will collapse. Similarly, meditative qigong practiced exclusively to develop spirit can weaken the body and damage physical health.

The Daoist sages did not separate daily life from spiritual life. They saw the physical world of nature (including the human body) as an expression of the inner guiding intelligence of qi. In their view, physical and spiritual cultivation deserve equal respect and care because they are part of a single, unfolding process. Following this tradition, Shing-ling-mei focuses on allowing the body and spirit to develop hand-in-hand.

*Jessica Miller has her qi
balanced by Master Wang*

Unless the food is predigested, it takes time and energy for your body to fully process the meal. Similarly, when qi from nature enters the body, it converts into the qi that we work with in qigong—the qi that fuels our metabolism and allows us to self-heal. This conversion happens as naturally as the digestion of food. By contrast, when our body receives human qi from an external source, it is receiving the equivalent of "predigested food" that is available for immediate use, as is. Receiving emitted human qi is especially helpful for people who are elderly, sick or weak in the same way that porridge would be a better food choice for them than steak.

When I first attended Master Wang's qigong classes, he introduced us to the concept of qi balancing and explained that, while in qigong practice we were learning to guide qi through our own body for our own benefit, during a qi balance session the master does this for us. These two practices complement each other because each has advantages and drawbacks. Through qigong practice we develop a tool that helps us balance our own qi and take control of our own health. We become more self-reliant and can access this tool wherever we are. However, to develop qigong skill takes time, patience and a level of dedication not everyone has. Also, there are times when all of us are tired or weak and can use an energetic helping hand. During a qi balance the work is done for us. Although we are relying on the services of another, we can simply relax and enjoy the experience.

DURING THE SESSION

During a typical qi balancing session with Master Wang, you lie face up on the table or perhaps sit in a chair and relax, while he gently adjusts your qi. Most sessions last about an hour, during which he alternates between actively moving your qi and passively feeling your body's response. Each session is tailored to the individual's needs at that moment.

Master Wang begins a session by perceiving the qualities of your life-force energy—assessing where the energy flow is constricted, where it is excessive or deficient and whether the energy is clear or has stagnant qualities. Once you are relaxed on the table, he closes his eyes and becomes very quietly focused, tuning his attention to the qi flowing within your body. He often sees as well as feels the energy flowing like light through the body. He also uses his hands to scan the body for qualities of energy that tell him where it is flowing or blocked, and whether the organs are congested or functioning well.

When the mind is sufficiently quiet and attuned, we all have the capacity to extend our sense of "inner" feeling or awareness to include things beyond our body. Just as there are frequencies of sound and light that extend above and below the range we normally perceive with our ears and eyes, we have abilities of perception that allow us to perceive things outside the normal range of our five senses. These abilities lie latent within us until something such as qigong inspires their development. They allow us to intuit subtle energies our five senses don't normally perceive. One of the hallmarks of qigong practice is the gradual appearance of abilities that result from developing the inner senses.

In the West, we don't have a vocabulary to describe the various qualities of subtle life-energy, yet they can be felt by many who are trained and sensitive. For example, doctors of Chinese medicine were traditionally trained to identify twelve pulses by feeling the wrist, while Western doctors feel just one. The qualities of energy expressed by these pulses are described in curious terms such as "thready," "sinking" and "floating."

As well as perceiving different qualities of energy, Chinese healers take note of external signs to indicate the nature of an individual's health problems. The color and coating of the tongue, the color of the skin on the face and under the eyes, and the condition of the palms are some of the signs that offer Master Wang immediate clues about how a person's energy is out of balance.

An energy master may use some or all of these methods to identify a problem. Although no single method is infallible, when used together they create a reliable composite.

Once he has made his assessment, Master Wang gets to work, balancing the flow and clearing away toxic energy. Just as no two great artists paint alike, it is safe to say that no two experienced masters use exactly the same methods in their work because subtle energy work requires skilled use of intuition. Nevertheless, traditional techniques have been passed down through apprenticeship, classes and texts of Chinese medicine and qigong. Some masters use only one favorite technique. Master Wang uses an array of methods passed on by his grandfather. For example, *five thunder palm* is a method of breaking up energy blockages and putting new qi into a person quickly, while *acupuncture without needles*, as the name implies, stimulates specific energy points along the body's meridians without requiring needles. Instead, it uses hand positions such as *sword fingers*.

Often during a session, Master Wang rests his hands gently on the shin or forearm of a client and leaves them there for awhile. This doesn't necessarily mean there is a problem at that site. Rather, he is using his hands as a contact point, while he withdraws his attention from the outer world and goes deeply into the awareness of subtle energies, opening their flow, smoothing their frequencies, guiding them gently with his mind through the inner universe of the body.

SENSITIVITY TO QI

What is subjectively experienced during each session varies from individual to individual and from session to session. No two sessions are identical, even for the same individual, because no one is energetically the same from one day to the next, or even from moment to moment.

During a session, some people experience qi as currents of flowing electricity, tingling, heat, light, colors, visions, sensations of floating and other altered states, as well as sensations of pressure, warmth or coolness. Some feel emotional release or a sense of being transported to the sublime. Others just feel more relaxed. Someone who is behind on sleep or hasn't been sleeping soundly will probably fall into a deeply refreshing sleep during the session. In general, when a session is over, a person feels light, relaxed and comfortable. This is the feeling of balanced qi flow.

People have naturally varying sensitivities to life-force energy. One person may have dramatic sensations, while another may feel nothing specific. Whether the sensations feel extraordinary or tame, there is nothing painful about it. After all, qi is the very sustenance of life. Normally, pain signals a block or lack of qi flow, and qi balancing relieves this pain. In certain cases, however, qi is so blocked that there is no feeling. In these instances, the resumption of qi flow may temporarily manifest as pain, much as a limb feels when it transitions from numbness to normal sensation. In this case pain is a welcome sign.

Sometimes people wonder if qi balancing is effective because they themselves are unable to feel the qi. Sensitivity is not the same as effectiveness. Master Wang always says it's not what you feel during a session that matters; it's what happens as a result. Many people reap considerable benefits without experiencing any dramatic energy effects during the session. Nevertheless, greater sensitivity to qi often accompanies faster results. This may be because sensitive individuals can feel things happening in the body during a session. Consequently, they are less prone to doubt and skepticism, which create electrical resistance.

FEELING IS BELIEVING

I was attending an all-day conference when I met a delightful Canadian man in a wheelchair. We sat next to each other at lunch and the man, whom I'll call

Ken, told me his story. More than two decades earlier, he had been in a serious car accident and suffered a spinal injury that left him paralyzed from the waist down. Then, two years before I met Ken, he discovered the services of a qigong master. After a year of therapy, he was able to feel the sensation of qi in his legs, but only during the therapy session. Unfortunately, Ken's job had recently forced him to relocate and since that time he had felt nothing in his legs.

I told Ken about Master Wang, and he immediately requested an appointment. I arranged to bring Master Wang to Ken's hotel room for a qi balance session the following day.

Master Wang examined the condition of the nerves in Ken's legs by scanning the energy field with his hands near Ken's body. He said Ken had enough nerve activity to walk again if he truly wanted, but it would take time and he would have to devote himself to practice. Then Master Wang began the session, using his own emitted qi to entrain Ken's qi and get it flowing through his legs and through the nerves of his spine. Master Wang worked for more than an hour as Ken sat in the wheelchair, eyes closed, smiling quietly. When the session was finished, Ken beamed and said he could feel the energy flowing in his legs during the session. Ken asked if Master Wang would return the following day for another session since it would be Ken's last day in Hawaii.

During the second session, Master Wang again worked on Ken's legs and spine. After nearly an hour, he pointed to Ken's right thigh and said, "Now see if you can move your leg. Test it."

Looking doubtful, Ken tried to move his leg. To my astonishment—as well as Ken's—his leg began to move back and forth, very slightly at first and then more resolutely. It was just a small range of motion, but his knee moved about three inches with each sweep. Ken's eyes sparkled. "This is the first time I've been able to move my own leg in twenty six years!" he exclaimed. Of course, this was just a small first step, but a significant one. "How should I practice?" he asked.

"Use your mind," Master Wang explained. "As often as you can, imagine yourself walking. Remember how it felt. See yourself doing it again. Feel it in your mind. Know that you can do this." He told Ken how to use his mind to lead qi up and down his legs and spine. He told Ken to slowly and gently coax the qi up and down, up and down for at least two hours every day. "At first it will seem like imagination, but slowly it will become real." He reminded Ken that the more he put trust and conviction into his practice, the faster he would progress.

Of course, not all qi balancings are so dramatic. Many people come to Master Wang with aches and sprains, headaches or stomach problems. Stacy, an old friend of mine, was visiting us while on a buying trip for her business. After a long day in town, she returned to our house feeling tired and congested. "I feel awful," she groaned. "This pressure in my head just won't let up. I know it's an imposition, but do you think Master Wang could give me a qi balance?

I found my husband at the computer, catching up on the Chinese rendition of the day's news. I knew it was his time to relax, but as I explained Stacy's condition, he pulled over a nearby chair. "Tell her to come here," he said. Stacy sat down in the chair beside him. "I'll show you what to do, and we'll do it together," he explained. He told her to focus her attention on the sensation of pressure in her head. "Don't have any special thoughts about it," he said. "Just slowly exhale while intending, feeling and visualizing the ball of pressure melting down through your body and out the soles of your feet."

Stacy closed her eyes, and he walked her through the instructions a second time. "Like a river, we'll wash it away," he said, as he moved his hand gently in the air in front of her, helping to wash the energy down through her body and out her feet.

When his hand got to her feet, Stacy's eyes flew open. "Wow!" she exclaimed. "It's completely gone! I felt it melting down through my body and disappearing as you were talking. Just like magic!"

"Not magic!" Master Wang explained. "Practice. Many years of practice."

HOW MANY, HOW QUICKLY

It is never possible to say just how many qi balance sessions a person will need to correct an imbalance. Depending on the situation, one session may be enough, or a series of sessions may be required to resolve the condition.

I remember watching a man from Germany arrive for a session, bent over double due to acute back pain caused by something he had done the previous night. Thirty minutes later, he walked out the door upright, pain-free and quite surprised, especially since this had been accomplished without physical contact.

I had a similar experience myself when, in a burst of enthusiastic spring cleaning early one morning, I reached too far too quickly and tore something in my back. The instant I felt hot, searing pain rip across my back, I literally dropped everything and got very quiet. I immediately began running energy through the area, as I had been taught in qigong. Within five minutes I felt fine. I put away my cleaning tools and began to fix breakfast. I thought I had fixed the problem, but about twenty minutes later I felt my back begin to tighten up. At that point, I asked Master Wang to check it out. He scanned my back by moving his hands lightly over the site of my injury. Then he gathered up a cloud of qi and with a sudden shout, threw it forcefully at my back with open palms. Without touching my back, he used *five thunder palm* to quickly break up the contracted qi and energize the area. Within minutes I was flexible and resumed my day as if nothing had ever happened.

As the preceding examples illustrate, the sooner an energy problem is addressed, the more easily it can be resolved. Once an ailment has had time to establish itself, it normally takes a series of qi balance sessions to clear it. An analogy commonly used in Chinese medicine is that of a flowing stream. Flowing water remains fresh, but when it stops flowing, it turns stagnant. Stagnant qi must be cleared away and replaced by fresh qi that can resume a healthy flow. An established disease process tends to create its own stagnant qi, like a toxic byproduct, which must be cleared in repeated sessions until a healthy flow is permanently reestablished. After each qi balance session, it is normal to experience considerable improvement, followed by some return of symptoms as the stagnant condition reasserts itself. Yet with each session, the improvement lasts a little longer.

Another analogy that helps people understand this process is to think in terms of habit. We are creatures of habit, and the energy patterns within us tend to be habitual. The longer a bad energy pattern remains in place, the more corrective sessions are needed before it is fully replaced by a healthy pattern. This analogy can clarify the process of "two steps forward, one step back" that describes the uneven road to recovery for some people. Of course, there are exceptions to every rule.

A SUDDEN RECOVERY

One day a young woman called to ask if Master Wang would qi balance her father in the hospital. He had been in the hospital for nearly two months, suffering from pneumonia, and his daughter was willing to do whatever she could to help him.

I scheduled the appointment and explained that I would accompany Master Wang so I could help with English. Much as I wish I were fluent in Chinese, I can only say that I translate his English into more understandable English. But translation aside, I like to accompany him because I learn many things during his sessions.

When we arrived at the hospital, the woman greeted us and led us to her father's room. His small head and shoulders rested like dry leaves on the pillows. It was difficult for me to guess his age because he appeared so gaunt and gray, but I would say he was somewhere in his sixties. Throughout the qi balance session, he remained unresponsive. Although I kept my thoughts to myself, my sense was that he was preparing to pass on.

When the session was over, his daughter asked Master Wang to return the next day, and every day thereafter until he was better. Master Wang explained that this wouldn't be necessary. He said, "Ask your father if he wants another session. If he does, I will balance his qi again in three days."

The next day, the daughter called to say her father felt better and wanted another session. So on the third day, we returned to the hospital. This time the man was sitting up in bed, smiling. I was astonished by his dramatic improvement. After the session, Master Wang again promised to return in three days.

The third visit was equally successful, and two days later, just nine days after Master Wang's initial visit, the daughter called me again with some good news. She explained that the doctors had told her they hadn't expected her father to recover. "Now they feel he's well enough to go home," she announced. "He's being discharged tomorrow!"

MIRACLES OF HEALING

Master Wang believes that, given enough time, enough qi and the right conditions, healing can occur in virtually all parts of the body. Science is learning new things every day about how the body heals itself, as well as how the universe works. Many things that seemed miraculous in the past are explainable today, and there is no reason to think this trend will change since we still have much to explore and understand about our universe and the mystery of healing. Master Wang agrees with those who say miracles do not occur outside of nature.

Rather, miracles are nature operating in ways that science has yet to understand.

Mary had been coming for occasional qi balancing sessions for several years when she suffered a small stroke. The first time I saw her after the stroke, she came through the office door hugging the wall with both hands just to keep her balance. She had come by taxi since she could hardly walk, let alone drive. Initially, she came for qi balancing three times a week. After each session, she felt lighter and more relaxed. As her balance improved, she tapered off to twice weekly sessions and then just once a week. Her condition improved quickly and steadily. Soon she was feeling fine and walking normally again. Then the great day came when she was well enough to drive. A card from her reads, "Thank you, thank you, Master Wang, for giving me back my life!"

Because Mary is considered to be in the high-risk category for stroke, she continues on medication and follows her doctor's orders. And she includes regular qi balancing as an important part of her preventive therapy. A year after her stroke, Mary came through the door with some exciting news. "Kathy, when I had my stroke, the doctors showed me a tiny spot on the MRI of my brain and said it was the site of the stroke. Well, guess what! They took another MRI yesterday and couldn't find the spot. Now, there's no sign of stroke at all!"

MAXIMIZING YOUR QI BALANCE BENEFITS

People often ask if there is anything they can do to help support the effectiveness of a qi balance session after it is over. Should they go home and rest or can they go out and play? Should they refrain from eating or can they go out to dinner with friends? The answer is they should feel free to do whatever they normally do, as long as it falls within the framework of life-supportive habits. Healthy habits of living (discussed in chapters 9 and 10) include such basics as eating a good diet, getting adequate rest and exercise, and maintaining an optimistic attitude. After a qi balance session, some people feel so deeply relaxed they just want to go home and sleep. Others feel recharged and ready to work. Both responses are fine, but remember to use common sense. If you come in the door feeling poorly and walk out feeling energized, don't rush out and play. Instead, let your body use that energy for healing itself.

Just as important as *what* you do is the spirit of pleasure with which you do it. Attitude plays a key role in healing, and it is especially important to pay attention to your attitude if you want to prolong the beneficial effects of a qi balance session. Feelings of worry, fear, self-pity, focusing on how sick you feel, harboring doubt that healing is possible or the method is effective—all these create electrical resistance that reduces the body's innate ability to heal itself.

Strange as it may sound, some people hold onto an illness because they feel it benefits them in some way. Sadly, they don't feel they deserve to be well. Of course this isn't true of everyone; nonetheless, emotions that perpetuate illness must be considered along with physical causes because both affect qi flow. The more relaxed and at peace we are, the more life energy flows freely and can do its work to maintain our good health. At the heart of all healing are love, acceptance and a simple willingness to be healed.

LEARNING TO BALANCE QI

Sometimes people come to Master Wang and ask him to teach them his method of qi balancing. They are not interested in taking qigong classes; they just want to learn techniques that will enable them to heal others. Master Wang replies that first you should consider how well you can feel and direct your own qi. Can you feel the quality of qi that is stagnant and cannot flow freely? Can you identify energy blocks at specific locations within your own body and clear them away? Before you can expect to sense and guide the qualities and flow of someone else's qi, you must be able to do so within your own body. This is not easy; it takes time, patience and dedication to practice. By practicing Shing-ling-mei qigong, you gradually develop these abilities and, in effect, develop your qi balancing skills.

Still, this is not the whole answer. Healing work, like learning Shing-ling-mei, involves more than mastering a set of skills. It is a collaboration between the "healer" and the "healed," who come together with the shared intention of promoting good health. What happens when there is no collaboration of willing intent, when an energy healer works on someone who isn't ready to be healed? Of course, the healing won't happen. Nobody can *force* healing on another because nobody actually *heals* another. Even the most extraordinary energy healer only provides the conditions for healing to take place.

The Man Who Thought He Had Cancer

Master Wang tells this story from his past to illustrate the powerful impact of the mind on our health.

During the 1980s, when Master Wang was still teaching in Shanghai, a man came to see him for emitted qi therapy. The man was in his late fifties and was so gaunt and thin that his family had to support him as he walked through the door. His family had made the long trip to Shanghai to look for someone who might be able to help him despite the fact that his local doctor could do nothing. The man had been diagnosed with stomach cancer. At the rate he was declining, he clearly hadn't much time left to live.

Master Wang lifted the frail man onto the table, while assuring him that, at the very least, he would be able to make him more comfortable. Then he set to work, closing his eyes and scanning the man's body with his hands. Again and again, he moved his hands slowly through the air above the frail body. Gradually a puzzled expression came over Master Wang's face. Saying nothing, he began to balance the man's qi, which was weak and erratic and in much need of strengthening.

When the qi balance was finished, Master Wang gave the man some surprising news. "I found no sign of cancer," he said. "Your doctor was mistaken. In fact, I feel you have no serious health problem at all!"

The man and his family were staggered by the news. After all, how could this be, when he was obviously in terrible shape?

"Your emotions are the culprit," Master Wang explained. "You are literally sick with worry. But now you can stop worrying and get well."

Master Wang encouraged the man to get medical confirmation of his condition so he and his family would feel convinced. He directed them to a nearby hospital where the man could be seen by a doctor and receive tests. The man, already feeling much better from the qi balance and his newfound hope, climbed off the table by himself and followed this suggestion.

A few days later, he returned to thank Master Wang and show him the medical report. Indeed, hospital tests confirmed he did not have cancer after all. With a new outlook on life, the happy man announced that he was already feeling well again and eating like a horse.

CHAPTER 9

Principles of Heart Wisdom

The Chinese sages knew that the way to live harmoniously in relation to one another and our world arises not from some external authority, but from the wisdom that resides within our own nature. They understood that happiness and well-being are determined more by our state of mind and heart than by anything else. They recognized that the seat of wisdom, intuition and higher intelligence resides in the heart. Master Wang echoes the ancient sages as he points out that although we can't always control our outer circumstances, we can always choose the attitude of our heart.

Anyone who spends time with Master Wang will be struck by his good-hearted nature and relaxed, informal style. His presence seems to put people at ease, and a genuine desire to help others shines through all he does. In a voice sometimes booming with intensity, at other times gentle as a cloud, Master Wang offers life principles that are simple, practical and much needed in our times. During class, he teaches attitudes that are synonymous with the essence of our practice:

- Relax
- Quiet your mind
- Understand the meaning of "enough"
- Love everybody, love yourself
- Be happy

These principles are not "extras" to practice along with qigong. They form the attitude we hold during practice. These attitudes create the fertile soil that feeds good qigong practice and nourishes harmonious living.

In the Chinese qigong tradition, a student couldn't simply knock on the master's door and expect to receive his teachings. He had to earn that privilege by proving the depth of his desire and dedication to learn. An aspiring student could expect to be tested by the master. Often he would be turned away, again and again, from the master's door. He might be left sitting for hours, waiting for meetings that never materialize. His rejections would carry no explanation, forcing him to figure out for himself what it was that he was doing wrong. Perhaps he was being rebuffed for a lack of humility. Perhaps he was being tested for his ability to be humble and persevering. If he demonstrated high moral character, a good heart, calm mind, a favorable attitude and keen desire to learn, then the master, seeing that he was worthy, might accept him as a student. This was the custom, handed down since ancient times.

In Shing-ling-mei qigong, Master Wang carries on the Wudang tradition of teaching wisdom principles by which to live. Happily for us, he doesn't adhere to the old methods of teaching and welcomes all who want to learn. Whereas, traditionally, principles were deliberately vague and shrouded in mystery, Master Wang brings them to the fore, emphasizing their practical value in helping us create balance in our lives and world. There is no set number of principles. Rather, they arise spontaneously in his classroom discussions as a reflection of what life is presenting at the time. The five principles introduced in this chapter are among the ones he stresses most often—principles of heart-wisdom that affect our practice of qigong, as well as our experience of life in general.

The first two principles, *relax* and *quiet the mind*, are necessary ingredients for all qigong practice. Even those who want to practice qigong at its simplest level must be able to relax and quiet the mind enough to become present. To go deeply into the practice, however, and allow it to transform us, we must experience a true change of heart. This comes by following such principles as remembering to love yourself and others, understanding the meaning of "enough" and practicing the art of happiness.

The principles Master Wang expresses are simple enough for a child to grasp, yet powerful enough to guide our lives. They can form a foundation for whatever we choose to do in life. These are not moral preachings but significant energy practices. By embracing them in your daily life, you will transform the quality of your qi. As Master Wang says, "When you live by these principles, you can do deep qigong!"

THE FIRST PRINCIPLE: RELAX!

Master Wang always takes time in his day to relax and do things he likes. In fact, it is rare for him to do something he doesn't enjoy. Whether it's reading the news, playing with his pet fish, hunting for bargains or dissecting and reassembling wrist watches, he moves through the day with a relaxed certainty about things. He has a natural sensibility for the flow of schedules—for which projects take priority and which can be left unfinished until later. Without a word, he teaches by example the meaning of "relax!"

For many of us, the idea of relaxing on demand may seem challenging, even contradictory. Yet we are all familiar with the contracted sensations of stress and the open release that comes with relaxation. As we learn through qigong to manage our subtle energy, we gain more control over this contraction/relaxation process. We move in the direction of being able to relax more deeply, more easily, more often and when we will it. By doing qigong and by not trying to accomplish too much in any given day, we can learn how to relieve stress in our lives.

Western scientists have discovered the chemical links between relaxation and our body's physiology. They explain in molecular terms why relaxation helps our health. But if you pose this question to Master Wang, he will look you in the eye and say, "Ohms!" No, he isn't referring to the mystical frequency of the universe; he means *ohms*, or electrical resistance.

Imagine the water of a river flowing through a set of locks, or gates, that open and close to regulate the amount of water passing through them. When fully open, these gates allow the water to flow fully and freely. As they close, the flow diminishes accordingly. We are electrical beings, and electrical resistance (ohms) works throughout our body in much the same way as these gates do in restricting the flow of water. The greater our electrical resistance, the smaller the volume of energy that can flow through us. When we feel stressed or our bodies are tense, our electrical resistance goes up. Just as everyone's physiology is unique, everyone's electrical resistance is different.

Through qigong practice, we learn to raise and lower our electrical resistance at will. Clench your fist and notice how the blood cannot flow freely through your fingers. Your knuckles turn white. Now relax your fist. The palm opens and blood flows freely through the hand once more. In this way, relaxation lowers electrical resistance, facilitating the free flow of qi that sustains our health and well-being.

Master Wang reminds us that not all forms of relaxation are equivalent. A numb leg may be very relaxed, but it is also limp and inert. A sleeping person may be relaxed, but at the same time also unaware. The purpose of living in a relaxed manner, as with qigong, is not to become oblivious, but to become more available to what is going on in the present moment. A relaxed and alert body puts you on the road to health. Its electrical resistance is low, and it is sensitive to subtle energy flow. A relaxed and alert mind is quiet and free of its usual chatter, and able to deal with the task at hand.

THE SECOND PRINCIPLE: QUIET YOUR MIND

During our early years together, Master Wang would sometimes look at me in the middle of a conversation and say, "Don't think too much." Astonished, I would swallow the urge to reply, "Well, *somebody* has to think around here." Inevitably, this happened when I was feeling stressed, imagining future challenges I was unsure I could meet. It took me awhile to understand that Master Wang wasn't condemning my analytical thinking or planning. He was bringing my attention to the fact that my mind was running away with itself, generating feelings of anxiety to which I felt I had to respond. He noticed I had lost my center of balance.

The mind loves to chatter about the past and future, and these thoughts cause our emotions to respond almost instantly. The result is that our body spends much of the time responding physically to things that are only in our mind. For example, when a friend does or says something we don't like, we tend to blame the friend for our hurt feelings, yet the true source of our disturbance is what our mind thinks about the event—the meaning we give it—not the event itself. Master Wang waves his hand to indicate in one ear and out the other. "Let it go." By paying attention to our thoughts and recognizing when they don't serve us, we can learn to quiet the inner chatter.

A quiet mind allows us the space to make choices, to act instead of react. A quiet mind, turned within and free from thoughts, is the doorway to an inner universe, available to all who have the time and interest to explore it. Upon its threshold, we encounter the sensations of qi flowing through the inner world of our physical body. As we move deeper within, we lose track of the physical and discover a wellspring of creativity and inner peace.

THE THIRD PRINCIPLE: UNDERSTAND THE MEANING OF "ENOUGH"

One of the favorite dwelling stations of a restless mind is the dream of having, doing, or accomplishing *more*. It might be having more money, doing more projects, or even having a greater capacity to help others… the list is infinite. The yearning for more may reflect a natural desire for growth and change. It might also reflect the mistaken belief that more is always better. Master Wang asks us to consider how much is really "enough" to maintain balance in our given circumstances. He encourages us to practice moderation, as the Chinese sages have done since ancient times. The ability to recognize how much is enough, to do what is sufficient for our purpose, desire or need without going to extremes, and the art of being satisfied with whatever we have, can serve our life well.

Practicing "enough" does not imply becoming average, mediocre, complacent or stagnant. It means more than letting go of stress or curbing the desire for excess. Understanding "enough" means skillfully knowing *when* to let go, *how much* to let go and *what* to let go. It means knowing yourself, your strengths and weaknesses, and using this knowledge to make wise choices in life. Only when you know your own parameters of "enough" can you find the best balance for yourself and work most effectively to serve others.

Sometimes we need to find balance in ways we least expect. Several years ago, a young man came to Master Wang with questions about some minor health issues. The man had a full-time job and as a hobby he taught singing to a choir. He sang daily and his choir was an important contribution to the community in which he lived. The man was in fair health overall, but his body was weak, and he seemed susceptible to every cold and flu that came along.

As the two men talked, I noticed that Master Wang asked a lot of questions about the young man's singing habits. In fact, he seemed more interested in talking about singing than about health. Finally, he explained, "When you sing, qi goes outside your body." He opened his mouth and gave a loud "ha-a-a-a" to demonstrate. "Your body's constitution isn't strong, and you lose too much qi every day through singing." Along with advice on ways to conserve qi while singing, Master Wang advised the man to sing in moderation, while paying more attention to the needs of his body. The man was dismayed by the news because even beyond the personal pleasure it gave him, he regarded his singing talent as an important means of social contribution. However, after a moment, he realized that by balancing his own health needs with his desire to help others, he would actually become healthier, happier and better able to serve his community.

THE FOURTH PRINCIPLE: LOVE EVERYONE, LOVE YOURSELF

When you feel loving, you help healing life-energy flow more fully and smoothly within yourself and between yourself, others and nature. But what is love?

"I love my mother." "I love my car." "I love swimming." "I love your new shoes." With so many meanings, is it any wonder we are confused about love? In our culture, we tend to identify "love" as those glorious feelings of attraction and attachment we have toward a favorite object or person. We might feel this towards our lover, our pet, a favorite toy or grandmother's strawberry shortcake. We experience this love because something pleases our senses and fulfills our desires and expectations. But what happens when the object of our love stops pleasing us, living up to our expectations and fulfilling our desires? We stop loving it! We get divorced, trade in our car and take up a new hobby.

This kind of love is really about obtaining personal satisfaction, about *getting* something from somebody or something. This kind of love is an automatic feeling-response that happens when the conditions are right. It flows when our desires and expectations are met and it stops flowing when they're not. So, if this isn't real love, what is?

Master Wang reminds us that real love is *giving*. Real love is to accept without conditions and to help or give to others without expectation of reward. It is the natural and spontaneous urge to help another. It is also an attitude we can choose to cultivate. The ancient Daoists recognized this aspect as a part of our inner nature. When we get in touch with it, we are in harmony with the way of life.

Because love is such a misused word, we can use the term "loving kindness" to refer to the giving of real love. When we act out of loving kindness for others and the world around us, this positive energy helps the world become a happier place. Like energies attract, so you tend to get back what you give out. Loving kindness, freely given, inspires feelings of connection and moves others to respond lovingly. The good feeling we experience in extending loving kindness to others is its own reward. Giving love in order to *get* it, however, is not real love and will not attract love in return. Rather, it tends to attract more of the same—the continued craving for love.

A woman in her fifties used to come for qigong. She often complained to me that she was continually sacrificing her own needs and pleasures for those of her husband and fellow office workers, but they never put her first in return. She came to class because, in her words, "I get so drained and here I feel nurtured." This woman was giving love to others with the expectation of return, and when the expectation wasn't fulfilled, she felt blaming and resentful.

Master Wang could feel how the woman's unmet expectations and negative emotions were creating an energy imbalance in her body. Not surprisingly, she suffered from multiple health problems. Fortunately, the story ends well because the woman, with the help of a therapist and steady qigong practice, came to realize that her real motivation wasn't love but a need to feel worthy. As she saw that she was giving in order to get, she began to include herself among those she "loved." As she was able to nurture herself more, her feelings of self-worth were restored and a genuinely loving bond developed between herself and others.

THE FIFTH PRINCIPLE: BE HAPPY!

When people ask Master Wang, "What is the most important principle of life?" he doesn't hesitate to reply, "Be happy!" He reminds us that, after all, we are here on earth to experience life and be happy.

But what is happiness? And how do we achieve it?

We all know the happy feeling we get when something in the outer world pleases our senses or conforms to our expectations. Like the garden variety of love described earlier, this happiness is a response to something we like. Research has shown that our general level of happiness is more dependent on our state of mind than on events in the outside world, or even our physical health. Happiness as a state of mind is an outlook we choose. We can choose to see the bowl of wontons half empty and feel disappointed that there aren't more, or we can choose to see the bowl half full and feel grateful for what we have.

One day Master Wang was visiting an ailing young woman in the hospital. The woman was fearful about her condition and depressed by the long recovery she faced. Master Wang reminded her to look on the bright side. After all, what she had wasn't terminal, nor was she paralyzed.

The woman brightened up considerably as she realized she was facing lesser challenges than many of the patients around her. Furthermore, she could use her long recovery time to work on the quilt she'd always wanted to sew but never quite had time for. "And don't forget to *smile*," Master Wang added before he left her room.

In qigong class, Master Wang teaches us about the importance of smiling. We smile as a natural result of being happy, but we can also reverse this order. When we put a pleasant smile on our face and leave it there, we begin to feel happier inside as a result. Try it for yourself and you'll see this is the case. By cultivating the habit of looking on the bright side with a smile, we can help ourselves cultivate the habit of happiness.

Loving kindness toward others and happiness go hand-in-hand. If my friend is weak and I help her become stronger—*I* feel happy. I smile at another's good fortune because it makes *me* happy. Quite simply, the more loving kindness we feel toward others, the happier we become. For this reason, Master Wang often encourages us to enlarge our sense of family. With an impish smile, he encourages us to consider our internal organs as members of our family. "They are a very good family," he says with a twinkle in his eye. And they work continuously on our behalf without competing, fighting or arguing with one another over different points of view. Instead, they work together harmoniously, sharing resources for the collective benefit of all.

And what about our human family? Can we welcome friends into our family? Can we extend loving kindness to the world as our family? Practically speaking, as we enlarge our sphere of loving kindness, we multiply our opportunities for happiness. As we practice acting for the collective benefit of all, we fall in line with the Dao, the way of living harmoniously.

Thinking With Your Heart and Feet

Master Wang says, "If you want to analyze, think with the head; if you want to tap into wisdom, think with your heart!" Thinking with your heart isn't just a figure of speech; it's a real practice. The HeartMath Institute in Boulder Creek, California, has spent decades researching the comparative effects of head-thinking and heart-thinking, and has scientifically validated the superior health and emotional benefits of the latter. Researchers at Heartmath have demonstrated that heart-thinking facilitates group cooperation, communication and understanding. The ancient sages would be pleased.

To think with the heart, quiet your mind and focus on your heart area (the middle dan tian) so qi gathers there. Maintain this focus as you open your heart and turn your thoughts to whatever situation needs to be addressed.

When a person gets angry, qi naturally rises to the head, leading blood with it. The face gets red, the person gets "hot headed" and clear thinking becomes impaired, if not impossible. What to do? Master Wang says, "Think with your feet." To think with your feet, shift attention to your feet (by feeling your feet from the inside) and keep it there while you count to ten. This draws qi down from the head and causes it to gather in your feet. Continue to feel your feet from within as you resume your thoughts.

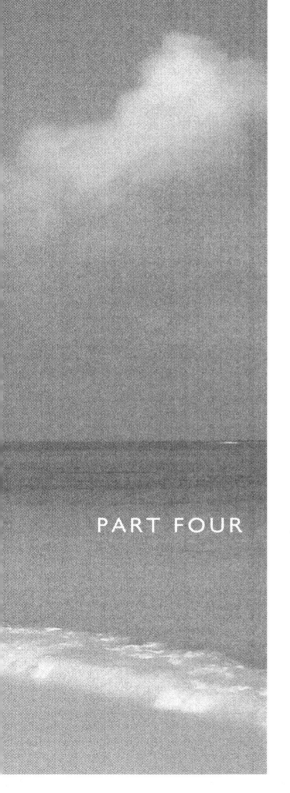

PART FOUR A PRACTICE OF LIFE

CHAPTER 10

The Qigong Lifestyle

Just as every chapter in a novel contributes to the plot, everything we do has meaning and significance in the story of our life.

Whether we are aware of it or not, we are "working with qi" twenty-four hours a day. We take in qi as food, water and air, and pass off qi as waste through our skin, lungs, bladder and bowels. At any given moment, qi is entering and exiting our body, as well as circulating within it. Furthermore, we are constantly manipulating qi through our actions, thoughts and emotions. We are, literally, life energy in motion, changing with every moment. And, like it or not, in each new moment, the quality and flow characteristics of our qi are either moving us toward greater health and harmony or away from it.

We might think of qigong as an energy practice we do for, say, an hour a day. But how much can we benefit from a daily hour of qigong practice if we abuse our energy during the other twenty-three hours? It makes sense for us to learn to manage our qi at all times—conserving it, nourishing it and directing it toward beneficial ends that can help us live more joyfully and effectively. In fact, learning to manage our qi is in many ways the same as learning to manage our life. This is what the qigong lifestyle is all about.

FOUNDATIONS OF HEALTH

Traditional Chinese medicine's single objective is to restore and maintain a balanced flow of healthy qi through the body. Toward this end, doctors apply acupuncture, herbs, qi massage, qigong and advice about personal diet and lifestyle. While acupuncture, herbs, qi balancing and qi massage require visits to a specialist, we can control our diet and lifestyle ourselves.

Although our genetic inheritance—the strength of our natal qi—plays a significant role in our health and longevity, it doesn't have the final word. After all, a person with a weak constitution who takes good care of the body's health can live a longer and happier life than someone else with a strong constitution who abuses or ignores his or her health. Master Wang believes that the most important influences on our health fall under our control. He puts cultivating a healthy attitude at the top of his list, followed by eating a healthy diet, maintaining a sensible schedule and practicing qigong daily. We examined the importance of managing thoughts and emotions in the last section. Here let's look at the other three items.

FOLLOW A HEALTHY DIET

There is so much contradictory information available about diet these days that many people are confused. Should I eat "high carbs" or low? Should my diet follow my blood type or my metabolic type? Should I combine certain foods and not others when I eat? Even our government's dietary guidelines for health go in and out of fashion based on the latest nutritional research findings. Do we even know what a wholesome diet is?

Once again, it is helpful to examine traditional wisdom. The Chinese have a long tradition backed by thousands of years of experience in using foods to promote good health and healing. By contrast, modern nutritional research is still in its infancy, having only recognized the significance of diet on health in the last few decades.

The Daoist tradition recognizes that all foods have energetic properties that affect the body's energetic balance in specific ways, just as herbs and medicines do, but in a milder fashion. For example, when I am feeling tired and depleted, Master Wang might tell me I need to boost my body's yin by eating more yin foods, such as seaweed salad or mung bean mushroom soup. Or he might suggest we simmer up a mixture of wolfberries (*gou-qi-zi*) and Chinese red dates (*hong zao*) for breakfast. These two dried fruits can be consumed daily as foods and are also prized "tonic herbs" used by the Chinese for centuries to nourish qi and address specific health complaints. For example, wolfberries are eaten to slow aging, improve vision, lower blood sugar and strengthen the liver, kidneys, heart and blood. This may seem like a tall order, but recent scientific analysis of wolfberries from Ningxia Province revealed that these berries contain more vitamin A than carrots, more vitamin C than oranges, are rich in calcium, protein and polysaccharides, and contain the highest level of antioxidants yet identified in any food. If you are searching for the most nutritious and healing foods on the planet, Chinese tonic herbs might be a good place to start.

In the Daoist view, methods of food preparation, as well as the art of combining specific foods to enhance desirable properties and cancel out undesirable ones, play an important role in diet. Cooking methods such as steaming and boiling are considered yin and enhance the yin properties of a dish, while yang methods such as broiling, baking and frying make the dish more yang.

Clearly, some knowledge of traditional Chinese medicine is required to become skillful in the use of appropriate foods to remedy specific imbalances in the body. Yet simple awareness that the energetic properties of specific foods and cooking methods can be used to offset the various imbalances in our bodies is enough for us to realize that a one-size-fits-all diet is unrealistic. Because each of us is unique, the specific foods that will best balance me will not be exactly the same as those that will best balance you. One person may thrive on raw foods, while another may do better on cooked foods. Some individuals do best with some meat in their diets, while for others vegetarianism is best. Furthermore, the best food for your body at any given time will vary as a function of your age and current requirements.

So, what constitutes a wholesome diet? Regardless of the specific dietary regime we choose, the foods we select from should be ones that will nourish us. Virtually everyone will agree that a wholesome diet is high in fresh fruits and vegetables and is without excessive fats, salt, sugar, artificial food additives and commercially processed "convenience" foods.

In the Daoist worldview, qi is what counts. Just as people can be strong and vital or weak and sickly as a result of their diet, so can the plants and animals we consume as food. It only takes common sense to realize that a carrot grown in soil containing the minimum nutrients for its survival won't have the same nutritional content or vital force as one grown in rich soil. Similarly, a carrot that's been sitting in storage for a month won't have the same nutritional content or vitality as one that's freshly harvested.

The Daoist view also supports eating local foods in season because the change of seasons expresses the changing balance of energies in nature. Those energies that are active during a particular season produce the foods of that season. Eating the "fruit" of that season helps us harmonize with the current balance of energies around us.

If you have the time and interest, you may want to embark upon the adventure of using foods as medicine according to traditional Daoist principles. *Healing with Whole Foods*, by Paul Pitchford, is a classic that provides the essentials for becoming skilled in healing through diet. For those who just want to upgrade to a wholesome diet, whole natural foods are a good place to start. By including a wide variety of fresh fruits and vegetables in your diet, while cutting back on sweets, sodas and highly processed convenience foods, you will be feeding your body the vital foods it needs to nourish itself.

Herbs in Traditional Chinese Medicine

Traditional Chinese medicine categorizes herbs as *inferior*, *general* and *superior*. *Inferior* herbs are hazardous to health if taken continuously, yet they are useful for treating specific serious ailments. They are considered inferior because they have toxic properties and must be used with knowledge and caution. In Chinese medicine, they are used only after gentler, more life-supportive approaches have failed. *General*, or *middle*, herbs work more broadly to strengthen the organ systems and nourish the body's vitality, while *superior* herbs nourish the body and also help it to self-heal by strengthening the immune system.

Superior herbs are also called *tonic* herbs because they nourish and strengthen various organs and systems. They are classified as yin or yang tonics, depending on the properties of qi they nourish, and as liver tonics, blood tonics and so on, depending on the nature of the deficiencies they address. As a group, they are non-toxic, healing and can be eaten continuously. However, because they do not yield the quick results many Westerner's seek and have come to expect from medicinal drugs, people often underestimate their long-term value. How interesting that what the Chinese view as medicines of "last resort" are the favored approach in the West, where toxic but fast-acting remedies are routinely chosen over safer, slower methods, such as beneficial dietary change.

MAINTAIN A SENSIBLE SCHEDULE

Daoist wisdom says our inner environment and outer environment function in similar ways. We can't separate ourselves from nature and ignore nature's laws because we *are* nature in action, manifesting as people. To maintain balance and harmony within ourselves, we must also maintain it in our surroundings. This means following a schedule that accommodates the rhythms of nature, a schedule that is sensible because it fulfills our body's needs. Unfortunately, in many countries today, it is difficult to follow a sensible schedule because a frenetic pace of life has become the norm. We are bombarded with such a wide selection of products and information that sometimes we hardly know which way to turn.

Down through the ages, Chinese sages who sought inner freedom would retreat to the mountains. They understood that, to find harmony and balance, one must take care of the body while letting go of the things that aren't necessary in life. While a mountain retreat may sound heavenly, it isn't an option for most people. Nevertheless, we can remain right where we are and use the ancient Daoist principle of moderation to establish a sensible schedule that works in our modern world. By providing for our body's needs and stopping when we've had enough, we can manage our life energy wisely and create a healthy life for ourselves.

Adequate amounts of sleep, rest and physical exercise, as well as eating regular meals, help bring the body's life energy into balance. By establishing a regular schedule for these things, our body benefits because it is a creature of habits—energy habits. Habits love routine. When we eat our meals at about the same time every day, our stomach knows when to prepare itself for the entry of food, and we start to feel hungry. When we go to bed at the same hour every night, our body learns the habit, and we feel drowsy at the appropriate time. Through routine, our body learns to automatically prepare itself for what lies ahead so it can flow comfortably with change, rather than be shocked by it. Through providing outer moderation, our body isn't stressed by extremes, and inner harmony prevails.

As with diet, there is no one schedule that suits everyone because everyone is unique. Some people do well on just five hours of sleep a night, while others need more than the eight recommended for adults. Some bodies require a steady routine that hardly waivers, while other bodies are quite flexible. What sort of schedule does your health thrive on? If you can't answer this question (and you've lived with your body for *how* many years?) then you have work to do. Start listening to your body and notice how it responds to different schedules. The news it has to tell you may be surprising.

DO REGULAR QIGONG PRACTICE

Just as the body benefits from a sensible schedule, it benefits most when qigong is practiced daily. Practicing qigong for fifteen minutes every day will benefit you more than practicing qigong for two hours once a week. To illustrate why this is true, Master Wang tells us a story about cleaning a piece of bronze.

There was a man who bought a lovely metal sculpture for his garden. He admired its beauty, but over time the gleaming surface began to tarnish and turn dark. He decided to clean it and spent two hours every Sunday polishing it up. Every Monday the sculpture looked better, but by the end of the week, it would be just as dark and tarnished as before. The man felt he was starting each week from the beginning again. He realized he would have to change his approach. Next he tried cleaning it a little bit every day. From one day to the next, the sculpture hardly looked different, but every day it was a little bit brighter than before. In time, the sculpture became glowing and bright. Now, with a little cleaning every day, the sculpture remained bright and beautiful. Like cleaning the tarnish from metal, it is easier to clear away a newly developed energy block than one that has been in place long enough to become an established pattern. Like keeping the sculpture bright, it is easier to maintain an open energy flow than to remove an energy block. Qigong creates the energy patterns of health. To make these patterns habitual, daily practice is best.

Practicing qigong daily has other advantages, as well. Many qigong practitioners lack the ability of traditional Chinese healers to identify subtle disturbances in the qi field even before the body shows something is wrong. Through frequent practice you will be more likely to catch undetected imbalances early on and correct them automatically, before they manifest as physical problems. Also, when you make qigong part of your daily regimen—like washing your face or brushing your teeth—you don't face the challenge of finding time to practice.

CHAPTER 11

The Fruits of Qigong

Virtually all prospective students ask themselves, "How will *I* benefit from Shing-ling-mei?" There is no single, fixed answer. Qigong is an extraordinarily versatile tool. On the physical level, Shing-ling-mei helps promote health and healing. On the mental and emotional levels, it helps strengthen the ability to focus and maintain equilibrium. On a spiritual level, it fosters insight and a loving heart. Each individual who begins to practice Shing-ling-mei can experience benefits in one or more of these ways.

Another common question is, "How fast will these benefits show themselves?" Of course, this depends in part on how much time you spend on practice. But beyond that, the attitude in your heart, your openness and willingness to trust and your commitment to steady practice—all play an essential role in the development of your practice and the benefits you reap. Some benefits, such as the alleviation of certain physical symptoms, can manifest in a matter of days or weeks, while spiritual benefits tend to develop slowly over the years.

Your goals for qigong, the intention you bring to your practice and how you choose to apply qigong in your daily life will help determine the kinds of benefits you derive from practice. This choice is up to you. Everyone is unique, and your results will be your own. Bring an open mind, an open heart, clear intention and a deeply dedicated sense of play… and see what happens.

PHYSICAL BENEFITS

Virtually every student has his or her own stories about the physical benefits derived from the practice of Shing-ling-mei. One of Master Wang's weekly classes has many seniors in it, including some in their eighties. I enjoy this class immensely because there is a youthfulness and joyousness in older people who become students again. It is wonderful to see seniors who have taken qigong for several years moving in class; they move with a grace and flexibility that easily surpasses many of the less experienced younger crowd.

Several students in this class reported their balance was much better after beginning qigong. One found she could jump up and down again—something she hadn't been able to do since injuring her leg and ankle many years before. An older gentleman noticed the prescription of his glasses had changed to a weaker strength. Another came to class one day saying that, instead of relying on the usual round of antibiotics to clear a recurrence of cystitis, she'd been able to overcome it by doing qigong. For seniors, decreased aches in the joints and limbs and increased flexibility throughout the body are especially treasured benefits of practice.

At the opposite end of the age spectrum are children. While Master Wang doesn't teach qigong classes specifically for children, he has qi balanced many. Children respond wonderfully to qi balancing. They have a natural openness and sensitivity to qi, without layers of emotional defense or skepticism that must be surmounted. I love to see the smiles on their faces as they feel the sensation of qi. I often dream of the benefits that could spring from classrooms of children playing with their qi through creative games involving simple movements and visualizations.

Young adults derive their own physical benefits from qigong. College students who attended one of Master Wang's workshops used qigong to improve their athletic skills. They found that the fluid, measured movements of qigong developed flexibility and increased their inner sense of body awareness, along with much needed mental discipline.

No age group is exempt from the depressive effects of stress on the immune system. A teacher who began practicing Shing-ling-mei because she suffered from frequent colds said, "Since I started qigong a year ago, I haven't had a single bout of flu, cold or bronchitis, and I used to get sick every three months!" Others who had more significant health problems experienced more dramatic healings, including freedom from years of chronic neck pain due to an old whiplash incident, diminished frequency of chronic headaches and disappearance of allergies.

Because Shing-ling-mei teaches us how to bring new qi into the body, circulate it and flush out stagnant or toxic qi, students quickly discover how to adapt these principles to resolve specific health complaints that arise from time to time, such as cramps, constipation, intestinal gas, heart palpitations, infections and more. I used it to resolve a frozen shoulder in half the time predicted by the physical therapist. Another student discovered after studying Shing-ling-mei for only a few weeks that he could get rid of a persistent headache within a matter of minutes by using focused attention to lead qi down from his head to his feet.

Master Wang counts doctors, taiji teachers, massage therapists and other energy healers among his students and clients. They explain that qigong benefits their work by increasing their sensitivity to, and understanding of, qi. One long-time student of hatha yoga who is also a doctor explains that qigong practice has helped improve his yoga skills and has enabled him to feel the qi, or *prana*, at work as he performs his yoga *asanas* and *pranayama*.

EMOTIONAL BENEFITS

During Shing-ling-mei practice, we focus on the sensation of qi as we lead it through the body. The act of focusing on the pleasurable sensation of qi flow automatically pulls our attention away from distracting thoughts and reconnects us with our sustaining life force, felt as calming energy. Our emotions naturally feel uplifted and relaxed. Over time, the pleasant relaxation and good feelings generated during practice spill into other areas of life. Many people report that they feel calmer, more "grounded" and less prone to stress or emotional upheaval. College and graduate students find qigong helps them deal with the stress of a heavy course load by bringing them back into emotional balance.

One student who had lost a relationship he really cared about was feeling lonely and bereft. Then he remembered what he had learned in qigong class about exchanging energy with trees—giving one's stale energy to the trees and taking in fresh energy from them. He began to do this practice regularly and found it had a grounding, nurturing effect. He said, "I discovered that when I'm quiet I can actually feel the living force of the trees. I can even feel the different energies of different trees. It's like communing with a giant and serene being. I needed a friend, and nature has become that friend."

My own first dramatic experience of how qigong came to my emotional aid was quite unexpected. I'd been studying qigong for a couple of months when I attended an environmental conference on Maui. I signed up for a guided nature walk through the upper rainforest. It was a watershed area not open to the general public, and in my enthusiasm to see this special terrain I neglected to read the fine print that said this tour was not for those afraid of heights. We walked along a narrow boardwalk that hugged the mountain slope, but every so often the path launched out into space as it crossed a ravine. With nothing but a wobbly two-by-four on one side that served as a railing, I was quaking in my boots. When we reached a very large ravine, I simply could not go on. I told the others I'd wait while they went on without me.

As I sat there by myself, I had to admit that if the thirteen others in my group could cross and I couldn't, then I had a problem. I decided to see if I could cross the ravine alone, at my own pace. I began visualizing calm scenes, taking deep breaths, humming soothing music—anything to keep my heart out of my throat and my knees from turning to mush. Nothing worked. It didn't consciously occur to me to try qigong, for I was still too new at it. Yet as my mind sought calming scenes, Master Wang's image kept coming into my mind, along with the phrase he used in class to help us guide the qi through our bodies: "open, down, open, down, open, down." Drawn to this like a magnet, I began to open to the energy flow and lead the qi down with my mind. I hadn't yet learned to identify qi sensation in the trunk of my body, but I noticed that, as I opened to the qi, I relaxed. The shift of my attention down to my knees, as I washed the qi down, lowered my center of gravity. Wow! Now I felt grounded.

By remaining focused on this simple qigong, I traversed the rickety bridge across the broad ravine. I caught up with the rest of my group, who were amazed I had so suddenly overcome my fear. With my newfound "tool" of qigong and confidence, crossing the same ravine on the way home was almost a breeze!

Many situations arise during the course of daily life that can be perceived as stressful or not, depending on how we approach them. One student who is the secretary to a litigation attorney in a high-stress environment says, "Since I began practicing qigong I can handle the stress better. My co-workers have noticed the difference in me. I remain calmer at work, and more focused." A man who does a lot of public speaking says he uses his qigong practice to ground himself whenever he's experiencing "butterflies" before making a major speech.

Another student, who had lost her husband to cancer, credits qigong with giving her the insight, strength and comfort to overcome grief and loneliness. She said, "It's quite ironic. I only began qigong because I wanted to encourage my husband to practice. We thought he could be healed, but he lost heart. Instead, I took the practice of qigong to heart, and it has transformed my life."

A woman who came for a qi balancing session at the suggestion of her son had been clinically depressed and on medication for an emotional imbalance for two years. During that time, she was unable to write a letter or get through more than a day without crying. When she returned the following week for a second session, I hardly recognized her. She was glowing. She grasped my hands in hers and said, "Kathy, I must tell you! You know I am a skeptical person, and I only came last week because my son insisted. But a miracle has happened, and I can't thank Master Wang enough. Since the qi balancing, I've felt fine!" She proceeded to tell me everything she had done during the past week—from weeding her whole garden to writing letters.

After the second qi balance, we never saw her again. I can't help but wonder whether her depression lifted permanently or returned and she never came back because she felt the qi balance had been only a "temporary fix."

Sometimes when the radical resolution of a long-standing condition happens suddenly, backsliding occurs as the body falls back toward its habitual patterns. This should not be cause for discouragement. When a condition becomes chronic, it is because there are habits or energetic patterns of some kind holding it in place. Even very negative patterns can become comfortably familiar in their way, and difficult to release. With steady qi balancings or qigong self-practice, healthy new patterns can be established that replace the old. To allow this time to happen, it is important not to get discouraged and give up too quickly. By being patient with yourself, persistent with your practice, and trusting in the process, you will help the body find its way back to balance.

Sometimes positive changes occur in areas where we least expect it. We can think of these benefits as the positive "side effects" of our systems coming into balance. Losing excess weight is a commonly reported side effect of qigong. One of Master Wang's students reported joyfully that he had lost twenty pounds of excess weight since starting his practice, without even trying to diet. He found he just wasn't eating as much. He suspected this was because he wasn't feeling as nervous since starting qigong. His chronic nervousness was a symptom of his body's imbalance, and as qigong helped bring his body toward balance, his nervousness diminished.

Over time, experiencing this kind of balance through qigong can help us become less fearful and reactive to life. When we are motivated by fear-based emotional responses, we don't tend to think of consequences beyond the satisfaction of our immediate need to get rid of the fear. Through qigong we become increasingly able to override such knee-jerk responses because we know "where to go." We have an inner resource to which we can turn for relief and upliftment. Our spark of divinity, our own inherent love, can become our basis for action instead of fearful reactivity.

SPIRITUAL BENEFITS

Spirit infuses all aspects of life. It imparts a sense of joy and beauty, of empowerment and serenity. Qigong helps strengthen the spirit in ways that manifest differently for each of us.

One of Master Wang's students explains his spiritual benefits from qigong this way: "Coming to class and learning about qigong, as well as practicing it, has helped me realize the spiritual unity behind all of humanity. This is a powerful thing. I now see that the Holy Spirit, by whatever name you give it, suffuses all of life. Some of my friends are so full of anger and fear that they don't trust any practice or perspective other than their own. I used to be the same way, so I know how they feel. Qigong is one of two practices that have helped me see and experience life differently. Now I see the spirit of love and acceptance everywhere; people just need to open and share it!"

Shing-ling-mei benefits us spiritually as well as emotionally by enabling us to move at will into altered states of consciousness—states of awareness in which our habitual identification with "self" recedes and we can more easily tap sources of creativity and inspiration. As a children's book writer, I want to inspire kids with a love of nature. But, like most writers, my river of inspiration doesn't always flow when I want it to. When I'm feeling creatively dry, the fastest means of shifting my state is to go outdoors and practice qigong (closing my eyes and imagining I am outdoors works as well). Within minutes, my heart is uplifted and I feel reconnected to my source. By holding this state for a few moments, I feel my creative juices flowing again and can return to my work with renewed direction.

Expanded states of consciousness attained during qigong practice lead some people to experience the *qi state,* as I described in chapter 7. Other people experience expanded states of consciousness when they receive a qi balance. One of Master Wang's clients says she comes for qi balancing to experience a state of consciousness that is normally unavailable to her. She describes it as a place of inner peace and bliss that surpasses all other experiences known to her, a state she has read about in spiritual texts but not achieved in her meditations. "It is a state in which my heart opens to a degree I cannot experience otherwise," she explains. "I would say it is the most meaningful experience of my life. It is such a gift to experience this state and realize we all have this capacity within us." Then she adds, "If everyone could experience this, the world would be a better, happier place!"

It is common for students of qigong to say such things as, "I can't place my finger on it, but somehow I know I've become a better person. I seem to have a broader perspective on life and I love myself more." These are signs of spiritual development. Growth of the spirit evolves slowly and quietly, unwatched, like a maturing fruit. It manifests subtly in our capacity to unconditionally accept whatever we might otherwise resist, to meet life fully and live from an open heart that can willingly endure pain as well as pleasure.

QIGONG'S MANY BENEFITS

Qigong can be used to:

- revitalize yourself
- improve health
- reduce stress
- ease pain
- balance emotions
- regulate physiology
- improve meditation
- further human development

Qigong has been used by people with the following conditions:

- anxiety
- asthma
- bronchitis
- cancer
- colds
- Crohn's disease
- chronic gastritis
- chronic hepatitis
- chronic pelvic inflammation
- cirrhosis
- cystitis
- depression
- diabetes
- diarrhea and constipation
- frozen shoulder (adhesive encapsulitis)

- gallstones
- gastric and duodenal ulcers
- headaches, including migraine
- heart palpitations
- hypertension
- lumbago
- menstrual problems
- muscle cramps
- paralysis from stroke
- pinched nerves
- rheumatic heart disease
- sciatica
- senility
- urogenital problems

CHAPTER 12

Sitting Down with Master Wang

If you have read this book straight through from the beginning, you now have a good foundation of understanding upon which to base your qigong practice. What are the main points you want to remember? Imagine you could sit down with Master Wang and have a question and answer session in which you could ask him to summarize some of the key points about qigong. What questions would you ask? What would he reply? In this chapter, you can enjoy such a conversation. While the English words are mine, the information conveyed is his. Hopefully, the answers to these questions will provide a helpful review while serving to distill your understanding of qigong and the energetic nature of health in general. Before you read Master Wang's answers, you might want to see how well you can answer these questions for yourself.

Q: What is qi?

Master Wang: Qi is the Chinese name for universal life-energy. It is the living, intelligent energy that forms the universe and brings life and animation to all things. I call it "life electricity" or "body electricity" because it has force field, flow, and frequency, yet it is different from common electricity because it also carries information. Qi is both the energy carrier and the message it conveys.

Q: What is qigong?

Master Wang: Qigong is a Chinese word that means working with life energy, or the discipline of working with life energy. It usually means working with *human* life-energy in ways that help people live better lives. It implies developing a skill or ability that takes time and patience to master.

Q: Are there different qigong styles and objectives?

Master Wang: Yes. People tend to work with qi in their own ways, depending on their abilities and objectives. Over qigong's very long history, thousands of styles have evolved, and they continue to develop today. People practice qigong for reasons that include healing the body from illnesses and injuries, maintaining and improving physical and emotional health, advancing spiritual development and improving sports and martial arts skills. "Hard," external qigong styles are forceful and are used mainly for performance advancement in sports and martial arts. "Soft," internal styles are gentle and are used mainly for health and spiritual development. It is difficult to generalize about qigong because one style can be so different from another.

Q: How ancient is qigong?

Master Wang: The Chinese have been working with mind-energy-body inter-actions for thousands of years. It is impossible to say exactly how ancient these practices are because they predate the written word. Ancient artifacts show qigong was practiced at least three thousand years ago, and oral history traces it back even farther to ancient shamans.

Q: What are the principles behind qigong's healing power?

Master Wang: First, keep in mind that you are a living energy process. This process is always moving either toward greater balance and better health or away from balance, toward disease. Second, remember that the disease process begins at the energy level before it manifests in the physical body, and that this is where healing begins as well. Third, remember that your "mind is the president" and "qi is the leader." This means your mind directs your qi energy, which in turn directs your physiology. In qigong, we use the mind to heal the body by working through the medium of qi.

Qi that is smooth, balanced and in adequate supply promotes good health. Qi that is blocked creates imbalances, excesses and deficiencies, which lead to disease. In qigong, we learn how to regulate ourselves mentally, emotionally, physically and spiritually, to unblock qi flow and promote healing on all levels.

Q: What causes energy blocks?

Master Wang: Energy blocks leading to illness can have many causes, such as injury, emotional stress, wrong foods, changes in weather or climate, wrong medicines and medicinal side-effects, poor schedule and wrong thinking or attitude.

Q: Is there a scientific basis for qigong?

Master Wang: The ancient seers and sages were the scientists of their day. In meditation they explored the subtle world of qi, mapped out its flow through the body and compared their findings with one another. Their testing grounds were their own bodies. They tested through their direct experience, and compared experiences among themselves. This is how they developed their understanding of energy healing and how diagrams of the body's energy meridians evolved. They also tested methods of qi healing on others, and observed the results. This exploration and testing continued down through the millennia. I am an explorer myself. I'm always exploring new ways to work with qi on myself. When I find something good, I share it with others.

Q: Does modern Western science have a way to explain qigong?

Master Wang: Medical science has demonstrated the electrical nature of life and has even developed machines that can locate acupuncture points and simulate some of qi's frequencies to relieve pain and help the body heal. Modern physics has determined that we live in a universe where thoughts, intention and emotion affect energy and matter, even at a distance. Years ago, people were frightened by energy healers and burned many as witches. Today people feel less frightened of these things because there are new scientific explanations for them. Doctors and nurses are more open to qigong, partly because they see that it works and partly because the scientific explanations give them confidence.

Q: What is the essence of Shing-ling-mei?

Master Wang: Shing-ling-mei is essentially a practice of body, mind and heart. I grew up with the Wudang tradition, which is a very complete and very broad tradition of qigong. It includes hundreds of different practices. Some are very complex; some can be dangerous. The principles and movements I teach in

Shing-ling-mei are safe and effective. Anyone can learn them and incorporate them easily into daily life. Most important, people can begin to experience benefits quickly.

Many qigong masters like to keep secrets to create an air of mystery and power. I'm not that way. I want my students to discover their own inner power. I want everyone to realize that we are all born with the ability to heal ourselves and lead happy lives. I offer tools and teach students how to use them. In Shing-ling-mei, I choose to focus on those aspects of qigong that help people transform their lives in positive ways. As we find inner balance and peace in our own lives, we also bring harmony to our imbalanced world.

Q: What will I gain by learning Shing-ling-mei?
Master Wang: By learning Shing-ling-mei, you will enhance your natural ability to self-heal. You will learn how to prevent disease and maintain a sense of well-being. These skills will help you maintain complete health—not just physical, but also mental, emotional and spiritual health. Healing isn't complete unless it includes all these aspects. What you learn from Shing-ling-mei can benefit you throughout your life and enable you to help others heal.

Q: How does Shing-ling-mei qigong differ from other practices?
Master Wang: There are so many forms of qigong that I cannot say how Shing-ling-mei differs from each one. However, I think Shing-ling-mei qigong is different from other popular practices in that it forms the *basis* for most of them. Is there another practice that includes all of the following attributes of Shing-ling-mei?

- *It can be practiced by virtually all ages, from ten to one hundred.*
- *It can be practiced by people in virtually all conditions of health.*

- *It enhances other valuable practices, such as yoga, taiji, meditation, massage, martial arts and sports.*

- *It requires no props or special equipment.*

- *It can be practiced virtually anywhere at any time.*

- *It is compatible with other health therapies, including Western medicine.*

- *Its benefits reach all areas of life.*

- *It's a pathway to inner happiness.*

- *It's fun and it feels very, very good! (Pain and stress have no place in Shing-ling-mei qigong practice.)*

Q: Does qigong have any drawbacks?
Master Wang: There are basically two. First, you must be able to focus your attention. Second, you must have patience and trust. Everyone is different. Some people feel qi immediately, others more slowly. Some people coordinate their mind and body more easily than do others. Some people get discouraged and give up practicing when they see others progressing more quickly. They don't have the perseverance to cultivate this discipline because they don't have the conviction they can do it successfully. Usually, once they begin to experience results, their conviction grows. It is also important to know that even those who find qigong difficult at first can nevertheless become adept over time.

Q: Do I need to study with a live teacher to learn gentle forms of qigong, or can I learn from a book or video?
Master Wang: The most important things are to develop a personal experience of qi and understand the significant role it plays in your life. Studying with a good teacher is helpful because the power of his or her qi entrains the

students' energy so they feel their own qi more quickly and progress faster. This is why most students feel qi more readily in class than when they practice at home. Nevertheless, good books and videos are sufficient for many people to establish a solid practice.

As students progress, they almost always have questions that require answers from an expert. For advanced students, contact with an experienced teacher is invaluable. Whether this contact is mainly through books, videos, the Internet or in person, the form of contact is less important than the quality of guidance. A teacher should be adept at navigating the world of subtle energies before attempting to guide others.

Q: Are there any people who *shouldn't* practice qigong?

Master Wang: People who are mentally unstable, people with a history of psychosis and people who are prone to negative obsessions or a desire to inflict harm upon others should not practice qigong. Some people have chronically negative thoughts that trigger negative emotions and emotional instability. It is important for such people to first bring their minds under control. If your mind can't become peaceful and focused, you will not be able to do good qigong.

Q: How safe is qigong?

Master Wang: Although most forms of qigong for health are safe and beneficial, not all forms of qigong are safe for everyone. Forms of "hard" qigong, including methods of forcing, compressing or "packing" qi, should be supervised by a skilled instructor. In addition, methods that bring a lot of qi to the head, such as certain meditations, can cause harm to students who don't have sufficient training to control their qi.

Once, a student who had been learning qigong "standing" poses from a master on the mainland came to see me because he had developed knee problems. His teacher told him to "push through the blockage" and keep at it. The student persevered, and his knees worsened until it was painful for him to walk. I told him to stop the poses immediately and gave him gentle healing exercises to promote qi flow through the knees. The knee problem quickly resolved itself. Problems such as this that develop through incorrect practice or incorrect guidance can be identified by a skilled teacher and remedied. Whatever form of practice you are in, it is important to let the teacher know whenever you are experiencing unusual discomfort or pain.

Q: How safe is Shing-ling-mei?
Master Wang: Shing-ling-mei is such a gentle combination of movement and meditation, and its goals are so life-enhancing, that it's hard to imagine it causing problems. However, even a walk around the house can cause problems if you have a fractured ankle or if there happens to be a banana peel under foot! If you have a medical condition it is always wise to consult with your doctor before beginning any new form of exercise.

Problems, when they do arise, usually stem from incorrect practice methods. For example, practicing when you are very tired or hungry can induce such side effects as dizziness, light-headedness or queasiness. Out of fear of doing something incorrectly, beginners can inadvertently tense their muscles so much they create pain.

Q: What is meant by "training qi is like training a dog?"
Master Wang: This means that when qi is led along the same pathway repetitively, it begins to flow that way automatically. Because qi builds through practice, the pathway that began as a small stream can gradually grow into a powerful river. This explains why someone can be very skilled in one specific energy technique, yet unskilled in others. It also explains why learning to control

qi may seem unimportant to someone whose qi flow is a small stream, but may assume great importance later on as the stream's power grows. For these reasons, I train students to control qi right from the start, and to guide it in many directions throughout all parts of the body, so pathways of qi flow remain flexible and build equally over time.

Q: What is meant by qi's "natural flow?"

Master Wang: In Shing-ling-mei qigong, we learn to move qi according to its movements in nature. By assisting its natural movement, rather than forcing it to go in unnatural ways, we get maximum results for minimal effort. And by working with qi's natural movement, we can adapt our qigong practice to enhance almost any task, from eating papaya to kayaking upstream. What is qi's natural movement? Watch the movements of wind and water. Wind and water are flexible and conform to the movement of qi. Those swirls, spirals, circles and waves express the movement of qi. There are no sharp angles, no sudden breaks and stops—just a swirling, billowing, circular, continuous flow.

Q: When I have learned the exercises in this book, will I be able to use them to cure my frequent pressure headaches?

Master Wang: Qigong has many ways to relieve pressure headaches. *Crane Flaps its Wings, Embracing the Universe* and *Feeding the Tree* can all be used to relieve headaches caused by blocked qi building up in the head. Each of these draws qi down through the body, away from the head, and helps open the neck and shoulders where qi often gets stuck. Nevertheless, the value of the exercises in this book is not in giving you a specific series of formulas, but rather in training you to sense qi and lead it safely and effectively where you want it to go. This is the secret of good qigong practice. Just following a series of steps, without being able to sense or lead qi with your mind, won't guarantee the result you want. Once you are able to feel and lead qi with your mind, you no longer need a formula. You can improvise and create an endless variety of solutions on your own.

Q: What is qi balancing?

Master Wang: Qi balancing is the name I use for what others call "emitted qi healing." I call it "qi balancing" because I use my qi and nature's qi to bring another person's qi into balance. I feel where their energy is blocked, and then open the blockages. I use my mind and qi to develop a smooth energy flow through their body. When qi is balanced, the body naturally moves toward health and the person feels very good.

Q: Can you balance everyone's qi?

Master Wang: Yes, but some people respond more dramatically than others. Everyone is unique, so what I can accomplish in one session varies. Energy sets up patterns. The longer a person has had an imbalance, the more sessions it usually takes to correct. It's like correcting a bad habit. Some habits are very persistent, while others straighten out quickly. Of course, if a person keeps doing something to perpetuate the imbalance—such as continuing to play sports with an injured knee or taking medication that generates side-effects— the imbalance will keep returning until the source has been eliminated.

Q: Are there things I should do or avoid doing after qi balance?

Master Wang: You should maintain a positive, relaxed attitude and avoid getting overtired. Do things that help your qi, such as being happy, following a good diet, keeping your body hydrated by drinking plenty of water, following a sensible schedule and loving your body. Remember, your body does the healing, so you want to help it along.

Q: Does medication affect qi healing?

Master Wang: Medication makes it more difficult for me to feel and see energy flowing in the body. If possible, you can schedule a balance just before your next dose, rather than just after. Please remember, I am not a doctor and I cannot advise anyone about medication. *Never stop or alter any medications without consulting your doctor.*

Q: Do you need to recharge after every qi balance?

Master Wang: No, but it depends on the circumstance. I will sometimes do two or three qi balancing sessions in a row, but usually not more than that. The amount of energy I use depends on what methods I'm using and on my energy level at the time. When I work with nature's energies, I can recharge as I work, but it depends on what I feel is needed in the moment. Every case is different.

Q: With what energies do you work?

Master Wang: I work with subtle energies from my body or the client's body and from nature. Different energies are available from each of these sources.

Q: How important is attitude to qi healing?

Master Wang: A person's attitude is extremely important for two reasons. First, it takes more energy for me to work on people who are skeptical or negative, because I must overcome their electrical resistance. Second, a negative attitude contributes to illness and, in some cases, can be the major cause of the disease. If a person is very fearful and anxious, his fear disrupts the body's qi flow. I can open the flow during a qi balance session, and the feeling of fear will temporarily diminish because of the new flow pattern. If the person walks out my door with new resolve to consciously release his fear and takes steps to reduce anxiety in his life, he is on the road to wellness. But if he resumes his normal fearful mind-chatter, the old energy pattern will quickly return because his attitude perpetuates it. For lasting healing, he must shift his attitude.

Q: What do you mean by "qigong has cumulative effects"?
Master Wang: Qi balancing and qigong practice both have cumulative effects. The longer you keep at it, the more quickly and easily the results come. This is partly because energy patterns are like habits. Through steady repetition you gradually dissolve old habits and strengthen new ones. As you train your qi, it obeys you more easily. It begins to flow naturally in the ways you've trained it to flow.

Q: Is emitted qi therapy something everyone can learn?
Master Wang: Everyone has the inborn capacity to use their qi energy to help others as well as themselves. Like any other talent, some people have greater ability than others, but everyone has some degree of ability that can be improved. Nevertheless, not everyone has the desire, patience and persistence to develop their natural ability into a useful skill.

Q: Is it possible to take on someone else's illness? I've heard conflicting things.
Master Wang: It is possible to take on another's symptoms, but you can learn how to avoid this. There are many methods of working with energy. You can learn methods that don't involve taking on another's bad energy and you can learn how to clear yourself if you accidentally do.

Q: Who is the healer?
Master Wang: It is a mistake to think that one person can really heal another. *Life's energy* is the healer within all of us, and each body does its own healing

from within. All anyone else can provide, regardless of the medical tradition or procedure used, is assistance to healing. Someone can help another heal by giving hope, encouragement, medicine and information. I can give energy and help establish healthy energy patterns in a person's body. But if a person doesn't want to heal, for whatever reason, nobody can *force* healing on another. Healing is like learning, loving and living—only you can do these things for yourself.

QUESTIONS TO ASK YOURSELF

The following twelve questions don't have answers because only you can answer them for yourself. By exploring your own answers, you will gain insight into how ready and willing you are to take part in your own healing and health welfare.

1. How healthy is my lifestyle? (Do I smoke? Eat a healthy diet? Get enough exercise? Get adequate sleep? Take time to play and have fun?)

2. Do I know what sort of schedule and diet my body thrives on?

3. How much responsibility do I take for my own health?

4. Do I have emotional problems?

5. Do I perceive myself as tolerant of others' views? Do I tend to carry grudges?

6. How strongly do I believe in the existence of subtle energy?

7. Do I believe I can learn to work with subtle energy effectively?

8. Do I believe that my thoughts and attitudes affect my health and happiness?

9. Do I have a positive attitude toward my life, and life in general? (How often do I feel grateful and appreciative? How often do I feel a victim?)

10. Am I able to maintain positive thoughts, either as images or mental dialog?

11. Why do I want to learn qigong?

12. What do I want to receive from qigong?

PART FIVE   THE EXERCISES

Let's Get Started

This section contains instructions for your starting position, six active qigong exercises and two sitting meditations. It also includes a closing qi massage to do at the end of your session. The final set of supplementary qigong breathing exercises is for you to try if you would like extra help learning to quiet your mind.

The practices are:

- *Starting Position*
- *Massaging the Qi Ball*
- *Standing like a Tree*
- *Feeding the Tree*
- *Crane Flaps its Wings*
- *Embracing the Universe*
- *Walking Between Heaven and Earth*
- *Stream of Colors Meditation*
- *Meditation of Choice*
- *Closing Qi Massage*
- *Supplementary Practice:*
  Qigong Breathing Exercises

HOW TO LEARN THE EXERCISES

Qigong involves learning outer movements of the physical body in conjunction with inner movements of energy. In class, Master Wang verbally describes the invisible pathways of qi flow, while demonstrating the body's physical movements. Students follow along as they learn inner and outer movements together. Those of you who would like to learn the exercises by watching Master Wang as he performs them outdoors can order the companion DVD. Once you become familiar with the movements by watching the DVD, you can continue to use the book as a helpful study guide.

You can also learn the exercises from this book alone. Learning any movement without watching a moving figure can be a challenge; trying to learn inner and outer movements simultaneously from a book can be daunting. If you find yourself struggling, you can choose to focus first on either the inner movements of qi or on the body's physical movements. Practice one aspect or the other first. Then, when you feel thoroughly comfortable with the aspect you chose, add the other.

Choose to learn first whichever aspect comes more naturally. If you are familiar with meditation, you will probably find it easier to begin by guiding the qi mentally. If so, stand or sit comfortably as described in *Starting Position* and follow the instructions for leading the qi, but without moving your body. If you have never meditated but love to dance, you will probably find it easier to learn the physical movements first. In this case, study the outer movements and practice them until your body can flow through the exercise comfortably. Then add your awareness of the qi's movement, as guided by your mind. Whichever aspect you learn first, the other will come more easily because each supports the other.

Is one aspect more important than the other? Master Wang reminds us that qigong is ultimately a mind practice; once you can lead qi effectively with your mind alone, you have a practice that will serve you even if your physical body cannot move. Because moving the body is secondary and serves to support moving qi with the mind, you can do these exercises standing, sitting or lying down.

Learn one exercise at a time. Practice it over and over until you can do it from memory, without straining to remember what comes next. Make the exercise a part of your day. You may want to practice it daily for a month or more before you feel ready to learn another exercise.

USING THIS BOOK

Each exercise includes a brief introduction that describes what the exercise does and how it helps you. Located below the introduction for each moving exercise is a string of small figures. These figures are like frames in a movie. Before you begin the active exercise, run your eyes along these figures several times to get a sense of the overall movement. Subsequent pages include diagrams and captions that use words and pictures to explain your body's physical movements and how your mind should guide the qi.

At the end of each exercise is a set of pointers. Many of the pointers apply to more than one exercise. Review these hints often. It is helpful to review them both before and after you perform an exercise.

Two of the exercises include "advanced" versions that involve leading qi along more than one pathway at a time. Thus, they require greater inner awareness. However, once you comprehend the internal movement, you will find these versions even more pleasurable and powerful than the initial version. You can think of them as providing additional support to the outer movement, while helping you expand your inner sensing abilities. Feel free to study these versions only if and when you feel ready. It is not necessary to know the advanced versions to develop the following skills.

The qigong exercises in this book will train you to:

- Develop your sensitivity to qi
- Lead qi with your mind
- Exchange qi with nature
- Use external qi to power your body's movements
- Circulate qi through your body to balance and remove blockages
- Flush away toxic qi
- Do qi breathing
- Strengthen the body's qi and improve its quality
- Strengthen the spirit

You won't need to master all the exercises before beginning to reap benefits. Still, it's important to resist the temptation to learn just one or two exercises and stop there. It is natural to become attached to an exercise that feels good and works for you, and it's normal to choose what already feels wonderful instead of struggling to learn a new exercise. But if you practice only one or two exercises over the years, you will build up certain energy pathways and not others. Your energy flow will tend to become automatic along certain pathways and not others, as though you were driving a car in the ruts along a well-traveled road. Remember, Shing-ling-mei aims to teach you flexibility and versatility, so that you can drive the car where you want it to go.

HELPFUL HINTS ON HOW TO LEAD QI

As you follow the instructions for the exercises, it may seem as if they are asking you to lead a discrete lump of qi through the body or between the body and nature. Yet qi flow is continuous. So how do you perceive this as you learn to lead qi? Although the fine, subtle energy of qi is neither like a suitcase nor a humpback whale, the following analogies may be helpful.

Imagine yourself in an airport's baggage claim area, picking up luggage. As you watch a specific bag being carried along the conveyor belt, you can also see the entire conveyor belt with your peripheral vision. Similarly, as you focus your attention on leading the qi along a certain route, you can simultaneously be aware of the larger pattern of its flow.

Now consider the annual migration of humpback whales. Humpbacks travel from Alaska to Hawaii and back every year, but they don't all arrive on the same day, nor do they all leave at once. They arrive gradually, starting in November. The population slowly swells to its peak in early March, yet some whales have already departed when others are still arriving. The population decreases just as gradually, and the last whales leave Hawaii's waters in June. Similarly, as you lead qi with the mind, qi concentrates at the point of your attention, but it does not do so immediately or all at once. It builds and disperses slowly over a broad area, as does the population of whales.

Although qi tends to concentrate where you focus, it remains part of a larger continuum—just as a wave remains part of the ocean. As you lead qi with the mind, you might perceive it as a subtle wave sweeping gently through your body, cutting either a broader or narrower swath—depending on your focus and intent. At first, you may find it challenging to focus your attention on even a single pathway of qi. But as you progress in your practice, you will be able to lead qi in several directions at once while also perceiving the larger patterns of circulation.

Playing with Focus of Attention

If you would like to experiment playfully with your focus of attention, try this short exercise.

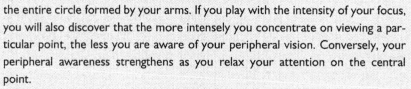

Hold your arms in front of you so they form a circle. Focus in front of you and let your eyes travel slowly around the circle. As your eyes pass over your fingers, wrist, forearm, elbow, etc., notice that at the same time your peripheral vision allows you to see the entire circle formed by your arms. If you play with the intensity of your focus, you will also discover that the more intensely you concentrate on viewing a particular point, the less you are aware of your peripheral vision. Conversely, your peripheral awareness strengthens as you relax your attention on the central point.

Now do the same exercise with your eyes closed. Use your inner senses to *feel* as well as visualize your attention moving around the circle of your arms. Again, you will notice that you can maintain a sense of the entire circle even as your attention travels around it. You can expand and contract your focus of attention to emphasize the entire circle or the point traveling around it. In general, when doing qigong, you want to maintain a relaxed attention that allows you to perceive both.

As a qigong practitioner, you will want to vary your focus of awareness at different times and for different purposes. However, don't be concerned if you are not yet adept at shifting and regulating your breadth of focus. Realize that qigong provides gentle training, and your abilities will strengthen with practice.

CREATING YOUR ROUTINE

Once you have mastered the exercises, how you practice them is up to you. You don't need to do all the exercises in one session, in any particular order or on the same day. You might choose to practice just one or two of the exercises at a time, or string them together to create a longer flowing movement. The important thing is to do *some practice every day*. Steady practice is the only way you can train your mind and condition the qi to flow as you direct it.

CLOTHING, PROPS AND SPACE

Shing-ling-mei requires no special clothing or props. Since it doesn't require moving around or fancy footwork, it can be done in a very limited space. It is important to be comfortable, but you really don't need much more than an arm's length radius around you. While standing in one place, sway and swing your arms freely in all directions. If you don't touch anything, you have enough space for your practice.

WHERE, WHEN AND FOR HOW LONG?

The most important thing about your practice location is that it should feel comfortable to you. Beginners should have a space that is quiet and free of distractions. It should not be too warm or cold, drafty or stuffy. You may want to unplug the phone so you won't be distracted during practice. As you become more adept at qigong, you will be better able to tune out distractions. Eventually, you can practice virtually anywhere. But for now, do whatever you need to do to make your space feel relaxing, safe and calm.

Practicing qigong outdoors in nature is especially wonderful if the above criteria for comfort are met. Don't practice in a strong wind because this depletes qi (a light breeze is fine, as long as it feels comfortable to you). Nor do you want to get baked by the sun, or wet and chilled from rain. Use common sense. Don't place yourself in conditions that are bad for your health, physically uncomfortable or non-conducive to a relaxed, quiet frame of mind. Don't practice when you're feeling uncomfortably hungry or full. If you're feeling angry or overtired, wait until you're feeling better before practicing qigong.

The best times to practice qigong are in the early morning when the qi is fresh and in the early evening as the day's energy quiets down and becomes restful.

Similarly, your practice session should last only as long as you are comfortable. A good length of time to practice is thirty minutes to one hour per day. If you can't manage thirty minutes, then twenty minutes or even ten is a start. (People who are trying to heal a life-threatening illness can aim for two or more hours of practice a day, divided into shorter periods and taking breaks whenever necessary.) Remember the importance of daily practice. It is easy to find ten minutes for a pleasurable practice, even when your day is full.

At the end of each practice session, whether you have been doing active movement or sitting meditation, it is good to end with a few minutes of qi massage. Your body becomes very open during qigong practice. A short qi massage helps close the "energy pores" of your skin after practice and evens out your energy.

Important Points to Remember

- The more relaxed the body, the better the qi flows.
- The more quiet and focused the mind, the better it can lead qi.
- The greater your trust in, belief in and dedication to your practice, the more effectively it works.
- Daily practice brings optimum results.
- Progress cannot be rushed. Some results will appear quickly, others slowly.
- Practice should be a pleasure.

PRINCIPLES OF PRACTICE

In Shing-ling-mei, you will learn to use external qi to power both your body's movements and the qi flowing inside your body. This helps conserve energy because you are tapping an external energy source rather than using your body's personal supply. How does this work? Think of a sailboat powered by wind. Wind blows into the sail, causing it to expand and fill out. The sail deflects the wind, sending it circling in new directions, while the wind provides momentum for the boat's movement. By steering the boat right or left, a sailor uses this momentum to guide the boat. In a similar fashion, external qi led by the mind provides wind-like momentum that you use to "steer" both your body and your internal qi in the direction you choose.

Shing-ling-mei employs a number of basic principles of movement. Although these are grouped below as "principles of body movement" and "principles of leading qi with mind and heart," they are really integral aspects of a single process in which mind and heart influence the body through the medium of qi. Don't be too concerned about remembering them as you practice. If you try to think about all of them during practice, your mind will be too busy and distracted for you to relax and do qigong effectively. Learning qigong is like learning to swim. You can't learn to swim by reading about the principles of swimming. You must get into the water and *do* it. Therefore, read through the following principles and consider them between practice sessions. Imitate them to help your body remember, and then let them go. If you like, choose one or two to focus on during your practice, until your body gets the feeling of them. Your body will learn these principles gradually, through correct practice.

Principles of Body Movement

1. Keep your body and muscles loose and relaxed, but not uncontrolled or limp.

2. Don't lock elbows or other joints; keep knees and elbows slightly bent.

3. Don't stretch any muscles or tendons to their limits—this constricts qi flow.

4. Don't strain yourself to copy someone else's posture or movement. Everyone's body is unique. Move only as much as you can without straining.

5. Body movements originate from the waist, or waist and torso.

6. Body movements spread outward from the trunk of the body, like a wave expressing the inner movement of qi. Follow the sequence of shoulder, elbow, wrist and fingers.

7. Use minimal muscular effort to accomplish your movements.

8. Move slowly during practice, as if you are in a slow-motion movie. The more slowly you move, the more effectively you can move qi.

9. In qigong parlance, the front of the body is called yin. When "yin opens," the front of your torso rounds outward, your arms fall backward and your weight moves to the toes.

10. In qigong parlance, the back of the body is called yang. When "yang opens," the back of your torso rounds outward, your arms fall forward and your weight moves to the heels.

11. As the body rises, your knees straighten and arms lower.

12. As the body sinks, your knees bend and arms rise up.

Principles of Leading Qi with Mind and Heart

1. Keep the mind relaxed yet alert, quiet yet not sleepy.

2. Focus your attention clearly, yet gently. *Feel* your body from inside.

3. Feel that you are part of a greater whole. (This allows qi to flow more freely between you and nature.)

4. Always lead stale or toxic qi down through the body, never up to the head or out the top of the head.

5. As a general rule, flush stale qi out of the body through the feet, or simply allow qi to leave naturally, on its own. If you are sitting with legs crossed, flush stale qi out the base of the spine.

6. When you send stale qi out of the body, always replace it with an abundance of new qi to avoid depleting yourself.

7. The momentum that drives most body movements begins as you bring external qi into the waist or torso (lower and/or middle dan tian areas) from either the front or back.

8. Allow yourself to experience only good thoughts and emotions during practice.

9. Intend that your practice will yield beneficial results.

10. Love your body and your organs. Love is the essence of healing; it opens energy blocks in the body. Love means accepting your body as it is, even though you may be working toward change.

11. Love others. Holding a grudge blocks the qi flow in your body. Forgive and let go.

12. Always end a qigong exercise by bringing qi down through your body, either to your lower dan tian or feet. Then just stand for a moment and *feel* your relaxed body, now vibrant and full of flowing qi.

FEELING QI

The two most common questions newcomers ask about qigong are, "What does qi feel like?" and "How long before I can feel qi?" Once you begin practicing qigong, your experience speaks for itself. You learn to recognize many sensations of qi and you feel different ones at different times. Commonly felt sensations of qi include:

- warmth or heat
- coolness or cold
- tingling on or just below the skin
- magnetic sensations
- electrical sensations
- heaviness or lightness
- inner movement or sensation of flow
- expansive sensation
- sense of fullness
- change in perception of body size, either larger or smaller

Some descriptions of stale, stagnant or toxic qi are *raspy, irritating, sludgy, jagged, unhomogenized, cold, hot,* or *painful.* Some descriptions of balanced, healthy and fresh qi are *smooth, soft, warm, invigorating,* and *homogenized.*

These sensations, and more, can be experienced as qi is moved in different ways and through different parts of the body. Some people feel qi immediately, while others take weeks or months to sense it. However, the speed at which you learn to identify qi sensations does not foretell your eventual degree of sensitivity or level of qigong ability. Regardless of how long it takes you to feel qi, the more time you spend on practice, the sooner you will feel it and the faster you will progress. Regular practice—daily if possible—is best. It is important, however, not to push yourself to gain results. Pushing, forcing and trying too hard run counter to the basic principles of qigong: to remain relaxed, tranquil and happy.

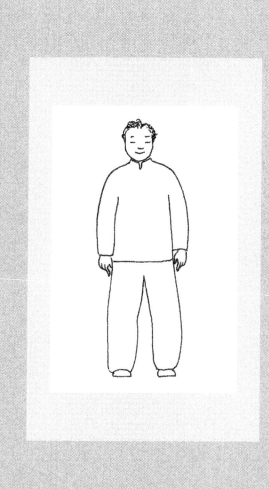

Starting Position

The Starting Position for all Shing-ling-mei exercises—both moving and still meditations—is simply to stand, sit or recline in a relaxed, balanced way. Human beings are energetically designed to walk upright between the polarities of earth and sky, so it is best to do the active exercises standing. If you cannot stand comfortably, it is better to sit. If you cannot sit comfortably, you can do the exercises lying down.

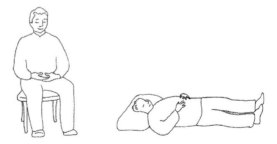

Starting Positions for Active Exercises

(a) Since standing correctly doesn't always come naturally, here are some simple guidelines.

Stand with your feet shoulder-width apart. Allow your shoulders to relax and hang loose. Don't stand in "soldier" position with chest out and shoulders back. Instead, allow your shoulders to round and chest to sink slightly. Let your stomach move naturally in and out as you breathe.

Breathe softly and gently through your nose. Don't clench your teeth, but keep your mouth closed, jaw relaxed and tongue in contact with the roof of your mouth. Drop your eyelids so your eyes are relaxed and partially closed, not staring.

Drop your chin slightly, and feel that all your vertebrae are resting comfortably, one atop the other, so you don't need muscle power to hold them in place. If your vertebrae feel compressed, imagine that a string extends from the sky to the top of your head, and your body is suspended from that string.

(a)

Curl your hips under your body, just enough so your lower back is straight and neither your belly nor your bottom protrudes. Relax your hips and belly. Be sure your knees aren't locked and your fists aren't clenched.

(b) If you are unable to stand, you can do qigong while sitting down.

Follow the same guidelines as for standing, but sit on a firm chair. If possible, don't lean back against the chair. Sit with your back upright and let your vertebrae rest as if stacked atop one another. You can also imagine your body is suspended from a string attached to the top of your head.

(b)

Rest your hands comfortably on your knees or in your lap, with palms facing either up or down.

(c)

(c) If you are unable to sit, you can do qigong exercises while lying on your back.

You can use a pillow to cushion your head or any other part of your body. Don't cross your legs. You can either bend your knees or keep them straight. Rest your hands comfortably on your body or at your sides. If you can move your arms, use them to guide the active exercises.

Starting Positions for Still Meditations

(d) Sit with legs crossed, or

(e) sit in a chair.

(d)

For practicing Shing-ling-mei, sitting cross-legged and sitting in a chair are both acceptable positions. Nevertheless, qi will flow through your legs more easily if they remain uncrossed. Whichever position you choose, keep your spine straight so you don't need muscle power to hold your vertebrae in place. Let your shoulders round and chest sink slightly. Breathe through your nose and let your stomach (not your chest) move in and out as you breathe. Keep your mouth closed, jaw relaxed and tongue in contact with the roof of your mouth. Drop your eyelids so your eyes are relaxed and partially or fully closed.

Rest your hands in your lap. To follow the traditional Daoist hand placement, men can place the left palm over the right palm (figure e). Women can place the right palm over the left palm.

(e)

Massaging the Qi Ball

Massaging the Qi Ball is a classic qigong exercise designed to help you feel your own qi and develop greater sensitivity to it. Qi gathers where you concentrate your attention. As you focus attention on your hands, qi concentrates in the hands and becomes easier to feel. Play with the qi ball, expanding it and contracting it. As you discover the qualities and sensations of qi through this exercise, it becomes easier for you to identify the feeling of qi in other parts of your body, as well as while doing other exercises.

1. Stand or sit comfortably in **Starting Position**, with knees unlocked and back straight, shoulders relaxed. Keep your eyes closed or relaxed with the lids slightly open ("qigong eyes"). Tell yourself mentally to "*relax, open* and *smile:*" Relax your body and mind. Use your inner feeling, intent and imagination to open your body's cells. (This helps you relax further). Put a gentle smile in your heart and on your lips. (This helps you feel peaceful and happy).

2. Rub your palms together until they feel warm and tingling. This helps qi flow into the palms and increases sensitivity.

3. Hold you hands in front of you, elbows relaxed and palms facing each other. Quiet your mind and place your attention gently on your two palms. Imagine you are holding a glowing ball of qi between your two hands.

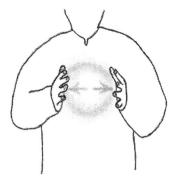 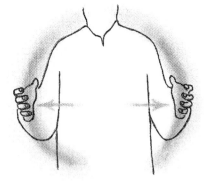

4. While keeping your attention on your palms, imagine you are inhaling (sucking in qi) through the center of each palm. As your palms inhale, move your hands slowly apart and imagine the ball of qi slowly expanding.

5. Move your hands slowly apart in a relaxed, steady manner. Expand the qi ball until your hands are about two feet apart. Focus on inhaling through your palms and let your lung breathing take care of itself.

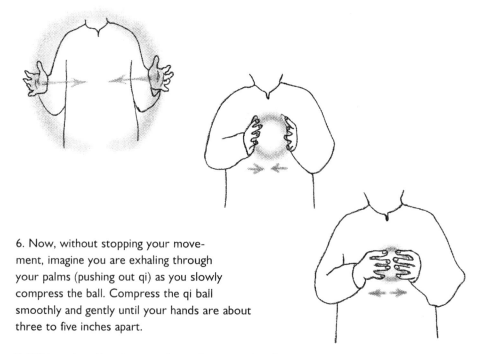

6. Now, without stopping your movement, imagine you are exhaling through your palms (pushing out qi) as you slowly compress the ball. Compress the qi ball smoothly and gently until your hands are about three to five inches apart.

7. Without breaking the even flow of your motion, begin to expand the ball again, as you inhale through your palms. Remember to stay relaxed and quiet. Do not strain your attention or tense your muscles. Keep your shoulders relaxed.

8. Repeat this sequence many times, slowly expanding the ball as your palms move away from each other, and shrinking the ball as your palms move toward one another. Gradually, your hands will begin to feel warm and tingling. See if you can notice a sense of suction between your palms as you expand the ball and a sense of pressure between your palms as you compress the ball.

  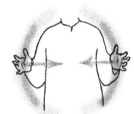

Pointers:

- *Remain relaxed, and try to refrain from "trying too hard" to feel the energy. The more relaxed you are, the more able you will be to feel qi.*

- *Keep your concentration focused, yet gentle. Your mind should be alert, yet tranquil.*

- *Remember, everyone is alive because of qi, so everyone can learn to feel it.*

- *You may find it easier to do this exercise when you synchronize the palm breaths with your lung breaths. This is fine if it helps you, but synchronization isn't necessary. The important thing is to keep your attention on your palms, not your lungs. Allow your lungs to breathe naturally and gently at their own pace.*

- *Be sure to look for a sense of resistance between your palms. It's as if like polarities are repelling each other when you bring your hands together, and opposite polarities are attracting each other when you move your hands apart.*

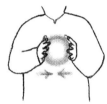

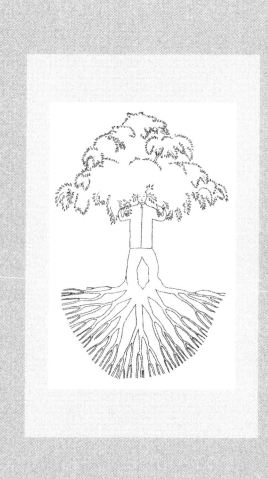

Standing like a Tree

Standing like a Tree is the first qigong exercise Master Wang learned from his grandfather. In this exercise you do not lead qi, you merely observe. This strengthens inner awareness that, in turn, strengthens the body's qi. Outwardly there is no movement; inwardly there is great activity.

Standing qigong—the practice of meditating while standing still—dates back to ancient times. It benefits posture and balance, increases inner body awareness and strengthens the legs and lower trunk of the body. It is especially useful for building stamina and strengthening the power of one's qi.

People who suffer from painful joints will do better to practice this exercise while sitting down.

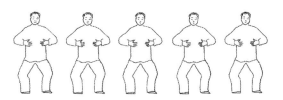

1. Stand as in **Starting Position** and *relax, open* and *smile*.

2. Bend your knees as far as is comfortable. If necessary, move your feet wider than shoulder-width to accommodate this. Your feet should be facing straight ahead, with your weight distributed evenly between the feet and resting mostly on the outer sides of the soles.

Maintain the vertical alignment of your spine by keeping your hips tucked under, so your bottom and belly don't protrude. (Don't tuck the hips too much, or you will need extra muscle power to hold them in place.) Extend your arms in front of you, with elbows and wrists bent slightly so they form an open circle, as if holding a giant sphere. Let your palms face your chest, with fingers spread slightly apart and relaxed. Keep your wrists in line with your forearms, so your hands don't flop like limp rags; nor should your hands be rigid.

When you feel your body is centered and structurally balanced, relax and sink into the position so your body feels anchored and "rooted" to the ground.

Arm height, foot position, and the degree to which you bend your knees will vary according to comfort level.

3. Hold the pose for as long as you can, *while remaining relaxed and without pain*. At first you may feel discomfort after holding it for only a few minutes. Gradually, with practice, you will be able to hold it for much longer. A good length of time to aim for is twenty minutes.

Breathe gently from your belly as you maintain quiet attention on your body. Feel your body from within and notice the various feelings and sensations that arise. Do not judge them, just notice them. You might experience qi as a tingling flow or perhaps as a vibrant energy field. You might notice only physical sensations, such as the feeling of blood flowing, or either warmth or coolness. You may also feel tiredness, weakness, stiffness or the burning sensation of tense muscles. If you begin to experience discomfort, make subtle adjustments by gently shifting the height of your arms or angle of your joints. This will relieve muscle fatigue and extend the duration of your practice session.

Your goal is to keep attention within the body and keep your qi channels open by maintaining relaxed muscles and joints. Just as a tree may appear rigid but is actually slowly flexing and moving, your body shouldn't be rigid either. You will find **Standing like a Tree** provides a lot on which you can focus your attention without letting thoughts distract you.

Pointers:

- *Don't try to DO anything during this exercise. Rather, be aware of your Being. Remain quietly present as you feel with your whole body. Sense your body from within, without forming thoughts about it. Notice what is happening in your body. You may become aware of sensations of qi flow. Perhaps you can feel where it seems to move freely and where it feels blocked.*

- *Keep the body and muscles relaxed. Use the minimal amount of tension necessary to maintain your pose. Let the mind become very calm and relaxed, yet alert and aware.*

- *Keep checking your body for tension. Consciously relax and release spots that become tense. Remember, it takes patience and practice to hold the pose while remaining relaxed.*

- *When you start to feel discomfort, focus on the area and move gently, as if tenderly massaging qi back and forth through the spot, keeping the qi flowing through the area. Envision the tight location becoming more open and soft.*

- *Be aware of your attitude toward your body. Regard it with loving kindness.*

- *Build your endurance gradually. Although some forms of this exercise teach you to push yourself to your limits, Master Wang emphasizes the importance of listening to your body, caring for your body and stopping when you experience excessive discomfort or pain.*

Standing like a Tree: Variation to Lower Blood Pressure

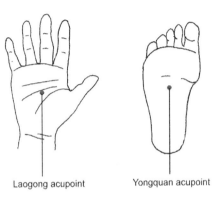

Laogong acupoint   Yongquan acupoint

Four large acupoints on the body—one at the center of each hand (*laogong acupoint*) and foot (*yongquan acupoint*)—are used in traditional Chinese medicine to regulate qi in the heart and kidneys. By combining focused attention and posture in the way described below, this variation of *Standing like a Tree* becomes a practice that is commonly used in China to lower blood pressure.

1. Sit on the front half of a firm chair with your back upright and relaxed. Place your feet flat on the floor, about hip-width apart. Relax your shoulders and elbows. Either rest your palms on your knees (figure a) or hold them in the air above the knees (figure b).

2. Imagine qi entering through the top of your head and flowing slowly down to the base of your spine, then down through your thighs to your knees. At this point, imagine qi flowing down from the laogong point at the center of each palm and joining the flow of qi that continues from the knees down into the feet (figure b).

3. Once you feel the qi has reached your feet, continue to focus your attention on the yongquan points in each of your feet, while imagining a column of qi connecting your hands and feet (figure c).

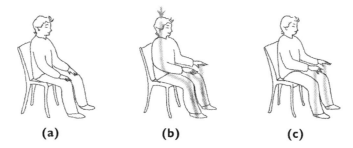

(a)   (b)   (c)

4. Hold this pose for at least twenty minutes every day. Your palms may either rest on your knees or hang a few inches above your knees with palms facing down. It is more relaxing to allow your palms to rest on your knees, but this can make it easier for your mind to wander. You can hold the qi more strongly if you keep your hands above your knees. Nevertheless, both ways are effective. If you hold your hands above your knees, you can relieve stiffness and maintain relaxation by shifting the angle of your arms gently from time to time. The exact height of your hands above your knees isn't important. You can vary it to maintain comfort during practice.

Pointers:

- *Just as our eyes use both central vision and peripheral vision to see, our "inner eyes," or inner senses, use central and peripheral awareness. After you have led the qi from your hands down to your feet, maintain your center of awareness on your feet. At the same time, use your peripheral awareness to maintain attention on the entire column of qi connecting your feet and hands.*

- *Do this exercise daily in order to achieve results.*

- *Whenever you feel pressure in the head, whether it is during qigong practice or while going about your day, imagine a soothing waterfall washing slowly down through your body from head to foot. Feel your feet from within until the sense of pressure is relieved.*

Feeding the Tree

Feeding the Tree clears your body of stagnant qi and brings in nourishing qi. One of the best times to practice this—or any—qigong is in the early morning, when nature's qi is fresh and invigorating.

In this exercise, *the tree feeds you* as you feed the tree. You practice replacing used, stale qi with qi that is fresh and nourishing, while taking advantage of the reciprocal relationship we share with plants wherein we each benefit from the other's waste energy.

Notice that, although the qi flows in a simple circle during this exercise, your body doesn't just stand there while your muscles lift your arms in circular fashion. Instead, your torso leads the movement of your arms, generating minimal muscular effort and maximum relaxation.

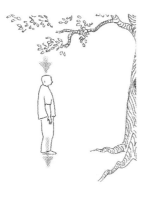

1. Stand in **Starting Position**, facing a large tree, and *relax*, *open* and *smile*. Imagine sky qi flowing down into your head and down through your body. Imagine the flow is flushing away stale qi and leaving fresh qi in its wake.

2. Imagine that your fingers are long enough to reach into the earth. They guide the qi as it leaves through the soles of your feet and flows toward the tree.

3. Continue guiding qi into the roots and up the tree's trunk with your long fingers.

As you do this, use your torso to help raise your arms. You do this by bending your knees in the motion of "sitting down," causing your torso to automatically straighten. Treat your arms and torso as one unit, so your arms ride passively upward as your torso straightens.

4. Imagine leading the qi as it rises up the trunk of the tree, nourishing the tree.

Continue the "sit down" motion until your torso is upright and your arms are horizontal.

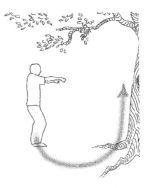

5. Imagine your long fingers guiding qi along the branches to the leaves of the tree.

As you do this, allow your back to arch slightly. This in turn lifts your passive arms still higher, so they rise over your head.

6. Imagine qi flowing from the leaves, coming down through the top of your head and into your body.

With arms overhead, let your elbows relax so your hands fall gently toward the top of your head.

7. Lead the qi down through your body. Imagine it flushing away stale qi and leaving fresh qi in its wake.

Guide the qi with your hands as they slowly move down toward your sides. At the same time, your knees slowly straighten until you are standing in **Starting Position.**

8. Feel you are one with the universal circle of qi flowing through your body, earth, tree and sky. Continue to circle the qi between your body and the tree as many times as you like before ending the exercise, once again, in **Starting Position.**

Pointers:

- *Guide the flow of qi with your fingers and hands, while allowing your torso (specifically, your waist and lower dan tian) to guide the movement of your body.*

- *Qi flows continuously, like a river, through nature and your body. Therefore, as fresh qi flows out from the tree and down through your body, be aware of it automatically displacing stale qi within your body and carrying it out through your feet.*

- *With this and all qigong exercises, finish by leading qi to your dan tian or your feet. Never lead qi to the head and leave it there because this can raise blood pressure.*

- *You lead qi with your attention.*

- *Negative emotions are not the same as waste. One woman made a daily habit of feeding her negative emotions to a sapling. After awhile, the poor tree died. No living thing thrives on negativity.*

Feeding the Tree: **Advanced Version**

When you feel comfortable with this exercise as described, you can enhance the power of this movement by leading external qi into your body during steps 2 and 5. This is a slightly more advanced version because you must focus on leading qi along more than one pathway at a time.

In step 2, you can become aware of a second path of qi that causes your back to round:

step 2

Without losing track of the qi you are leading with your long fingers, consciously bring a small amount of qi in through your front at the navel. Move it straight through your waist. As it nears the inside of your back, let it radiate downward toward your sides until it merges with the qi that is being led underground by your long fingers. Like wind filling a sail, the flow of this qi causes your back to round slightly and your arms to drop forward.

In step 5, you can become aware of a second path of qi that causes your back to arch:

step 5

While keeping track of the qi you are leading with your long fingers, consciously bring a small amount of external qi in through the small of your back. Move it straight through to the front of your body and guide it up through your chest, your neck and face and down through the center of your body (step 6). In this way, it creates a loop as it joins the main stream of qi flowing down through your body in step 6. As in step 2 above, this qi flow is like wind filling a sail that causes your front to round and your back to arch slightly, raising your arms upward.

step 6

Crane Flaps its Wings

Crane Flaps its Wings helps train you in the basic principles of body movement that are optimal for moving qi. Your whole body undulates smoothly and gracefully as it responds to, and encourages, the circular flow of qi.

Crane Flaps its Wings helps ground your energy and gets it flowing smoothly through your body. At the same time, you are learning how to consciously lead qi with the mind, circulate it through the body and exchange it with nature. This exercise is especially good for the lungs.

Since ancient times, the crane has been known in China as the bird of happiness and longevity. Famous for its love of dancing—in all seasons, at any time of day and at any age—the crane inspires the works of artists, poets and qigong masters alike.

1. Stand in **Starting Position** and relax, open and smile. Imagine you have long fingers that can reach deep into the earth.

2. With your long fingers, pull earth qi up through your legs and into your dan tian area—the belly region near your navel.

As your hands guide the earth qi up to your dan tian, your knees bend, and your body sinks slightly.

3. Imagine new qi coming in through the small of your back and merging with the qi in your dan tian.

This back-to-front flow causes your front to begin rounding outward. Your knees remain bent.

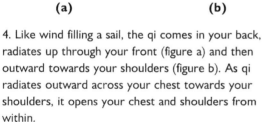

(a)   **(b)**

4. Like wind filling a sail, the qi comes in your back, radiates up through your front (figure a) and then outward towards your shoulders (figure b). As qi radiates outward across your chest towards your shoulders, it opens your chest and shoulders from within.

As the qi moves up your front (figure a) your back begins to arch; as your back arches, your arms are naturally lifted higher and your palms rotate outward, facing away from your body. As your chest and shoulders open (figure b), your arms naturally move outward as if you are parting a giant set of closed curtains. Your knees remain bent.

5. As the qi reaches your shoulders, sense sky qi flowing down from above, helping to steer the course of your qi downward.

195

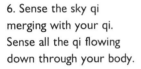

6. Sense the sky qi merging with your qi. Sense all the qi flowing down through your body.

As sky qi enters your body, your back becomes upright. Your arms slowly lower as your hands guide the qi down through your body. As your arms lower, your bent knees slowly straighten.

7. As your arms return to their normal resting position, keep your palms parallel to the earth until you feel all the qi has reached your feet.

8. Once the qi has reached your feet, relax your hands and allow your fingers to drop to your sides. If you like, you can imagine stale qi leaving through the soles of your feet, like faint wisps of smoke.

9. This completes one flap of the crane's wings. You can repeat this movement, continuously, as many times as you like before closing.

Pointers:

- When you imagine your fingers becoming long and reaching deep into the earth, you are using a mental tool to help you gather earth qi and pull it up into your body.

- Move slowly, as if you are moving in slow-motion.

- Notice that you are not standing still and flapping your arms, which would take muscle power. Rather, you are using qi that is coming in through the small of your back (the "back entrance" to your lower dan tian) to help power the movement of your torso. The torso, in turn, lifts the arms.

- Because qi is like a cloud, you may sense it as covering an area inside and outside the skin. This is fine. Don't be too concerned about boundaries. Realize, however, that the part inside is what helps clean and revitalize your cells.

- Don't let the arms just drop to your sides; always move in a slow, even and controlled manner.

- Remember to end all qigong exercises by leading qi away from the head, to the dant tian or the feet.

Embracing the Universe

With *Embracing the Universe*, you develop further what you learned in the last exercise about using the lower dan tian to power your qigong movements. Here, you learn how yin and yang sides of the body work together to absorb external qi and circulate it through the body.

This exercise also teaches you how to send good qi out of the body without losing control of it. Energy attracts like-energy to itself. By keeping your attention on the good qi you send out, you can bring it home to your body multiplied.

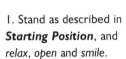

1. Stand as described in **Starting Position**, and *relax*, *open* and *smile*.

2. Imagine qi coming into the front of your body. Feel it move straight through the dan tian area, from front to back. When it reaches the inside of your back, sense it radiating through the skin, expanding your back as it moves toward your sides.

Your back rounds gently and your elbows open.

3. The qi swirls around your sides like a gentle cloud, moving inside and outside the skin.

Your back rounds further, causing your arms to circle around your sides until they near the front of your legs and feet.

4. Pull new qi up from the earth and let it merge with the qi that has swirled around your sides. Bring it all up through your feet and legs to your dan tian.

Your hands move up toward your dan tian as your knees slightly sink.

5. Imagine new qi flowing in through the small of your back and merging with the qi in your dan tian.

Your rounded back straightens. Your knees remain bent.

6. As the qi reaches your front, it expands and radiates outward from center.

Your front begins to open as your back begins to arch. You arms begin to extend and open in a welcoming gesture.

7. Feel the qi opening and expanding your heart, lungs and shoulders.

Continue until your arms are fully open (don't lock your elbows), your front is open, and your entire body is gently arched like a bow. Bend only as far as is comfortable without tensing your muscles.

In doing this gesture, it is normal to feel as if your qi is flowing out into the universe. Be aware that you want to increase your qi, not deplete it. To do this, you want to maintain attention on your qi, rather than allow it to go forth on its own and dissipate. To keep track of your qi, you can imagine you are unfurling a giant and beautiful net that is also a part of you.

8. Like a fisherman, use your imagination and intent to unfurl the giant net and capture new qi. As your arms open in welcome, expand the net as far as you like into the vast universe. Then slowly gather it in, along with the new qi it has attracted.

9. Imagine the net compacting and concentrating the new qi it has gathered.

Your back begins to straighten, bringing your arms toward each other.

10. Bring the qi into your body as if guiding a cloud or a gentle shower of rain.

As you bring it into your body, your back straightens further. Your hands move toward your head, and your palms gradually turn to face downward.

11. Mentally guide the qi down through your body. Sense it nourishing and revitalizing every cell.

Your hands guide the qi slowly downward through your body. As your arms slowly lower, your knees slowly straighten.

12. As qi passes through your heart, feel your heart open like a flower.

As your heart opens, your hands, now level with your chest, move very slightly out to your sides while your elbows simultaneously move closer to your sides.

13. As qi flows gently toward your feet, imagine new qi displacing old.

Move your arms slowly down toward your sides. Keep your palms parallel to the earth until you feel that all the qi has reached your feet. Then relax your palms and allow your fingers to hang at rest.

14. You have now completed one cycle of *Embracing the Universe*. You can repeat these movements as many times as you like without stopping. When you finish, stand quietly for a few moments in **Starting Position** and feel the new vitality that fills your body.

Pointers

- *Don't be concerned about leading qi along exact pathways. Move as if you are leading a soft, luxuriant cloud. Go for the feeling of it.*

- *Let your breathing take care of itself. The real respiration is the exchange of qi with your surroundings.*

- *This is a wonderful exercise to do outdoors. If you are doing it indoors, you can close your eyes and imagine you are outdoors, standing on the grass or beach under the open sky.*

- *Remember to maintain a continuous, steady, slow motion.*

- *As you practice this exercise, become aware of the interconnected flow between you and the universe. As you embrace the universe, the universe is embracing you. Just as you are a body within the unlimited universe, an unlimited universe also exists within your body.*

- *In step 6, be sure you don't simply send your qi off into the universe so it is lost. Maintain conscious control of it with your attention so you can reign it back in!*

- *Open your heart with gratitude as you open yourself to the universe. Like-energies attract, so the better the quality of your qi, the better the quality of the qi it attracts.*

- *Feel supported and nourished by the qi you are moving through your body. Remember, you are connected to the life-sustaining energies of the universe at all times. By using your intent and desire, you can call upon these energies.*

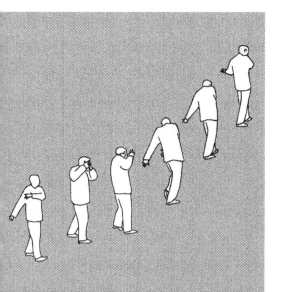

Walking Between Heaven and Earth

Walking Between Heaven and Earth is an exercise you can do with enjoyment as you take a leisurely walk outdoors. In this exercise, you bring new energy from the universe into your body to cleanse and invigorate your vital organs as you flush away toxins.

Walking qigong is wonderful for cleansing specific organs such as the lungs, liver, spleen, stomach, pancreas, kidneys, intestines and reproductive organs. It is also good for hip and leg problems, and has become famous throughout China for helping people heal from cancer.

Walking qigong can also be done without walking at all. As with the other qigong exercises in this book, you can stand, sit or even lie down. In the following pages you will learn to do the movement standing in one spot. When the movement becomes familiar to your body, you can coordinate it with walking, as explained on the last page of the exercise.

Here **Walking Between Heaven and Earth** is performed without moving your feet. Run your eyes along the strip of figures below and notice:

- how the arms create a horizontal "figure 8" pattern as they sweep from side to side. One loop of the "8" is on the right side, and the other loop is on the left, much like a baton twirler.

- how the upper body turns from right to left, guiding the movement of the arms.

- how the body rocks gently from side to side as the weight shifts from one foot to the other.

- how the torso turns from side to side while the lower body remains facing forward.

1. Stand in **Starting Position** and *relax, open* and *smile.*

2. Imagine your arms reaching out to your right side and gathering a clear ball of healing qi.

Twist your upper body to the right as your weight shifts to your left foot. At the same time, gently reach out with your arms, as if gathering qi.

3. Imagine guiding healing qi into your upper chest.

Slowly turn to face forward as your weight shifts back to both feet. The qi enters your chest as you face forward.

4. Move the qi slowly down through your torso toward your left leg. Sense it cleansing your organs, delivering nutrients as it picks up waste.

Continue turning your upper body to the left as your weight shifts slowly to the right. Your hands help guide the qi's flow downward.

5. Imagine the qi flowing down your left leg. As it nears your foot, sense that it has become gray and dingy from the waste it has gathered.

Continue shifting weight into your right leg, and continue turning left as your hands move slowly downward.

6. Imagine yourself moving the waste out the sole of your left foot. See yourself sweep it away and sense it dispersing behind you.

Lift your heel as stale qi flows out your foot. Let your arms swing back in a sweeping motion.

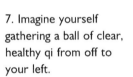

7. Imagine yourself gathering a ball of clear, healthy qi from off to your left.

Continue circling your arms up to your left as they form the left loop of a horizontal "8."

8. Imagine bringing this qi into your upper chest.

Slowly turn to face forward as your weight shifts back to both feet. The qi enters your chest as you face forward.

9. Move the qi slowly down through your torso toward your right leg. Sense it cleansing your organs, delivering nutrients as it picks up waste and toxins.

Continue turning your upper body slowly right as your weight shifts slowly to the left. Your hands help guide the qi's flow downward.

10. Imagine the qi flowing down your right leg. As it nears your foot, sense that it has become gray and dingy from the waste it has gathered.

Continue shifting weight into your left leg, and continue turning right as your hands move slowly downward.

11. Imagine yourself moving the waste out the sole of your right foot. See yourself sweep it away and sense it dispersing behind you.

Lift your heel as stale qi flows out your foot. Let your arms swing back in a sweeping motion.

12. Imagine yourself gathering another ball of clear, healthy qi from off to your right, and bringing it into your upper chest.

Continue circling your arms up to your right as they form the right loop of a horizontal "8." The loop is complete as you bring your arms near your chest. As your arms near your chest, your body turns to face forward.

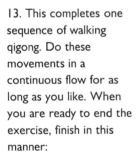

13. This completes one sequence of walking qigong. Do these movements in a continuous flow for as long as you like. When you are ready to end the exercise, finish in this manner:

14. Guide the qi down through your torso to your dan tian. Sense it as a glowing ball, shrinking smaller and smaller as your body absorbs its goodness.

Bring your hands to your dan tian. Remain facing forward with weight on both feet.

15. When the clear qi is absorbed, lead any remaining traces of stale qi down your legs and out through the soles of your feet.

Move your hands out to your sides and slowly lower your arms to resting position. Stand for a moment and feel your radiance.

Pointers:

- *When you reach out to gather a cloud of new qi, reach with your mind as far and wide as you like. Reach to the stars—how much qi you gather is up to you!*

- *Remember to visualize healthy qi as clear, and stale or toxic qi as dingy or sooty.*

- *It is helpful to follow the qi's movement with your eyes. This helps keep your attention focused on qi flow. When the qi is flowing inside your body, watch it with your mind.*

- *Don't try to synchronize your breathing with the movements or you will walk too fast. Allow yourself to breathe naturally and evenly as you walk at a slow, even pace.*

Walking Version

When you have mastered the stationary version of **Walking Between Heaven and Earth** it becomes very easy to adapt it to walking. Simply lift your entire foot instead of just your heel (see steps 6 and 11) and place your foot down one step in front of you instead of setting your heel down in the same spot. The rest of the movements are the same.

Variations

Once you have learned this exercise you can adapt it to suit a broad range of health concerns. For example, you can bring new qi into your chest to wash your lungs, or bring it in lower down to address a stomach or pelvic problem. You can use your mind and intent to strengthen an organ or shrink a tumor.

Stream of Colors Meditation

Stream of Colors Meditation uses the healing qualities of color to cleanse and revitalize five vital organ systems in your body. As you practice this meditation, you develop your ability to sense temperature, visualize color and sense the placement of your internal organs. With practice, you will be able to use your inner senses to identify the condition of qi within your organs.

In traditional Chinese medicine, the Five Element Theory (also called the Theory of Correspondences) describes qi as it goes through transformative processes within the body and in nature. All of nature's processes can be described within the context of five basic elements: water, wood, fire, earth and metal. These elements correspond to specific organ systems, sounds, colors, climates, seasons, emotions and so on. The elements, and therefore organs, exist in sequential relationship to one another, according to their place in the transformational cycle of life. In **Stream of Colors Meditation**, you will follow this sequence as you lead qi from one organ to the next, filling each with clear, bright color.

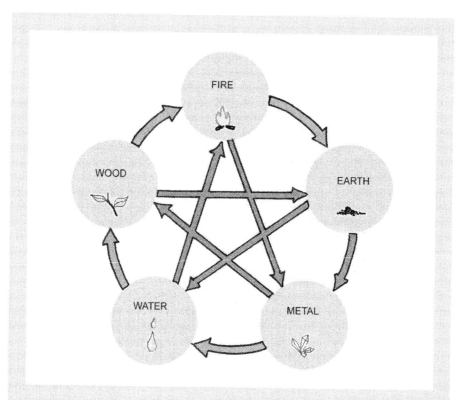

This figure describes the cyclical transformations of the five elements as qi flows throughout nature and within the human body: Wood fuels fire. Spent fire creates ashes and decomposed matter, which form earth. Earth yields metal as minerals and bedrock. Bedrock holds, conveys and distributes water through the earth's crust. Water feeds trees, which in turn fuel fire.

Each element has a nourishing or inhibiting influence on the others, depending on the direction of transformation, shown by the arrows. The outer arrows represent the nourishing cycle; the inner arrows describe the inhibiting cycle.

Each of the five elements has many corresponding qualities and aspects—the three on which you will focus in this meditation are organs, colors and temperature. Visualize colors of fresh qi as clear, pure and bright. Sooty or dingy colors are associated with stale or toxic qi.

Classic texts assign the color black to the kidneys. If you want to visualize black, choose a deep, clear black. Master Wang suggests you visualize the kidneys as clear, deep purple. He also suggests you use warm pink rather than hot red when visualizing the heart. This is because today's modern lifestyle tends to overexcite the heart, and hot red is inflammatory, while warm pink is soothing. In Shing-ling-mei, we cleanse the heart by visualizing it as an opening lotus flower. We do this to avoid leading qi upward through the heart, which can raise blood pressure. Moving qi through the heart in a horizontal or downward direction is fine.

ELEMENT	WATER	WOOD	FIRE	EARTH	METAL
ORGAN	kidneys	liver	heart	stomach	lungs
COLOR	purple	green	pink	yellow	white
TEMPERATURE	warm	cool	warm	warm	cold

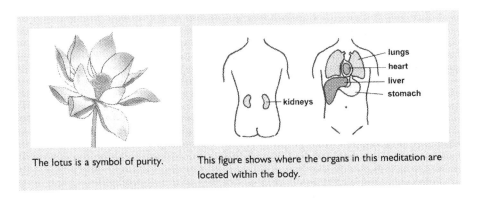

The lotus is a symbol of purity.

This figure shows where the organs in this meditation are located within the body.

1. Sit comfortably. Either sit in a chair with feet on the floor hip width apart, or sit with legs crossed. Rest your hands comfortably in your lap. Follow the starting position guidelines. When your mind is calm and quiet, you are ready to begin.

2. Close your eyes and imagine a vast, luminous cloud of qi high above your head. Imagine the cloud descending toward your head, thickening and condensing as it enters through the top of your head.

3. Imagine the cloud condensing into drops of warm water that begin to flow from the base of your skull, down your spine. As the warm flow nears the small of your back, it spreads laterally into both your kidneys.

4. Imagine the warm water transforming to light in your kidneys. Your kidneys fill with warm, clear purple light. See the light dissolving away impurities and debris within the kidneys. Feel your kidneys soften and expand as this warm purple light nourishes them.

5. When your kidneys are full, visualize the stream of light flowing from your kidneys into your liver. See the liver filling with clear, cool spring-green light—the color of fresh young leaves. Feel your liver soften and expand as the cool green light dissolves away toxins. See the gall bladder, tucked beneath your liver like a small ball, filling with cold ice-blue light.

6. When your liver and gall bladder are filled, imagine the light flowing into your heart. Envision your heart as a lotus bud. As the flowing light enters your heart, its relaxing warmth coaxes the bud to open. See the pure pink petals of the lotus unfurling, nourished by warm, clear pink light. Feel quiet love and appreciation spill forth from your opening heart. When the heart lotus has fully opened, guide the light onward.

7. From the heart, the light flows down to your stomach. As it enters the stomach, see the stomach filling with warm, clear yellow light—the soft yellow of a baby chick's down. Feel the stomach relax and soften as it is nourished by warm yellow light.

8. Now see the light flowing up to your lungs. See the lungs filling with cold white light, as clean and pure as moonlight. Feel the lungs soften and expand as they are nourished by the cold white moonlight.

9. From the lungs, imagine the light flowing down to the kidneys, already filled with warm, clear purple light. Imagine it moving through the kidneys again, flushing any remaining impurities down the base of the spine, down the legs, out the feet and away into the earth. (If you are sitting cross-legged, send the impurities directly out the base of your spine into the earth.) Only the impurities drain into the earth, like small trails of cloudy gray smoke. Your organs remain filled with fresh, healthy qi. Visualize them clear and glowing, each with its own color. Feel you body at peace, filled with tranquility and vitality.

10. When you are ready, open your eyes. Either continue with active qigong exercise, or complete your session with the closing qi massage.

Pointers:

- *Other traditions, or even personal intuition, may cause you to associate specific organs with colors that are different from the ones given in* **Stream of Colors Meditation**. *This is fine. Traditions are guidelines arising from methods that are effective for many. They are never the only methods. We are all creative healers, and traditions themselves evolve and change over time. The main thing is to hold heartfelt conviction that the color you are using benefits the organ. Remember to visualize dirty, stale or toxic qi as murky, cloudy and dingy, and to visualize the colors of fresh qi as clear and bright.*

- *Don't worry if you can't sense temperature and color at the same time. This is normal. The mind's abilities develop gradually. At first, you may choose to focus only on color as you practice* **Stream of Colors Meditation**. *Next you can focus only on bringing differing temperatures to the different organs. When you feel ready, you can combine them in one meditation.*

Meditation of Choice

Meditation of Choice is your opportunity to practice any of the active exercises in your mind as a sitting meditation. Choose an exercise you have committed to memory so you won't be struggling to remember the steps.

The great advantage of training your mind to lead qi without the aid of physical movements is that you can practice qigong even when your body is unable to physically assist you; just *imagining* the physical movements and their associated feelings of qi flow become enough to actually move qi. By doing the exercises with your mind alone, you train your mind as you test your own progress: can you feel qi moving within your body as you will it to, without moving your physical body? Do you feel a shift in your physical and emotional state as a result of this meditation?

1. Pick a comfortable **Starting Position,** preferably sitting in a chair with your legs uncrossed (it is very difficult to move qi through your legs when they're crossed), and close your eyes. *Relax, open and smile.*

2. Begin to guide qi with your mind in the same way you do for the moving exercises. The only difference is that your physical body isn't moving. You may, however, find yourself swaying slightly or turning your head or waist slightly, as you lead the qi with your mind. This is fine.

Do not sit and watch a "movie in your mind," as if you were viewing it from the outside. Rather, focus on your own *inner feeling.* As you imagine yourself performing physical movements, focus on seeing and feeling the qi as it flows in relation to those movements. Some people find it easier to do the moving exercises as seated meditations because they don't have to coordinate the physical movements with their mind while also guiding the flow of qi. You may sense your physical body as sphere-like, with qi circulating through it, and between it and nature. As long as you maintain control of the qi by leading it in the directions you choose, this is fine. Your sense of the inner qi flow is what counts. Your goals are to develop sensitivity to the flow of qi within, to learn to guide it and to allow it to transform you.

3. As you practice, you can experiment with using the assistance of body parts such as a finger, your chin or the movements of your closed eyes to help guide qi with your mind. For example, try using one finger to lead qi as you visualize it moving through your entire body. The finger, resting in your lap, may move no more than an inch in any direction, yet it serves as a pointer, helping your mind stay focused as it leads the qi where it needs to go. After you have performed several repetitions of the movement in your mind using one finger to guide the qi flow, try performing several more repetitions while leading qi with your chin. After this, or during another practice session, see how well you can do the exercise without using any physical movements to assist you.

At some point, you may reach a stage in which your mind becomes very tranquil, empty of thoughts yet attentive, and the qi will seem to flow smoothly through the movements on its own, for as long as you intend it. Be sure to maintain an open heart. You will feel the deeply satisfying sensations of the qi as it swirls within your physical structure; in fact, you may seem to feel it outside your body, as well. Let awareness of your body's physical boundaries diminish and even vanish as you become fully attuned to the blissful, undulating dance of qi.

4. When you are ready to end the session, be sure to bring yourself back to normal awareness gently and gradually, as if waking from a refreshing sleep. Follow this meditation with the **Closing Qi Massage**, to ground yourself before assuming daily activities.

Pointers:

- *Once you can move qi effectively with your mind and inner senses, you will discover that, as a rule, smaller outer movements (of the physical body) yield more powerful inner movements (of qi). This is because physical movements, while mechanically assisting qi flow and helping keep the mind focused, can also take some of your attention away from the qi itself. Subtle physical movements allow more concentrated attention to remain on qi.*

- *With a quiet mind, tranquil awareness and open heart, focus on the flowing qi. Allow yourself to experience the patterns of flow in whatever way feels best. At times you may experience light and color, or even sound. When your system is harmonized and in balance, you will feel the sensation of qi as a deeply satisfying, smooth hum.*

- *As you become more proficient, you will notice the building of energy during meditation, as if the flowing waves and circles of qi are charging a battery. It's as if you are becoming filled with the juice of vitality. When you feel filled with the exquisite hum of qi, allow your mind to become utterly still. You may feel at rest in a vast ocean of well-being; you may even feel at rest as a vast ocean of well-being.*

- *Remember to have patience. Allow your results to develop over time.*

Closing Qi Massage

Closing Qi Massage is simple, pleasant and effective. In the qigong tradition, practitioners perform qi massage on themselves at the end of their practice session. This helps bring the mind out of meditation into normal awareness and closes the body's energy pores, which were open wider than normal during practice.

Do **Closing Qi Massage** at the end of each qigong practice session. You may do the following nine steps exactly as described or create a similar version of your own.

1. Rub your hands together until they are warm. Then place them over your face, one on each side of your nose, and massage your skin gently in outward circles, about five times.

2. Using the sides of your thumbs, massage down the sides of your nose three times.

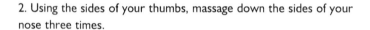

3. Cover your eyes with the palms of your hands so the center of each palm is over each eye, and circle gently. Feel the warmth radiating from your palms as you do this.

4. Spread your fingers apart, and massage your scalp with the fingertips of both hands. You can "rake" your fingers straight through your hair from front to back, or you can make tiny circular motions with your fingertips as you work your way from front to back.

5. Massage your ears, one with each hand. Hold each ear between your forefinger and thumb, and massage it thoroughly from top to bottom.

6. With fingers together, cup your palms over your ears so that the tips of each middle finger nearly touch each other at the base of your skull. Thump with your first and second fingers against the base of your skull.

7. Rub your hands together to generate warmth and place your palms over your stomach. Circle them slowly around your navel while feeling their soothing warmth.

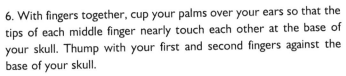

8. Rub your hands together again and place them against your kidneys. (Place one hand on each side of your spine at the base of your ribs.) Massage the skin over your kidneys vigorously for a moment, then leave your hands in place and feel their penetrating warmth.

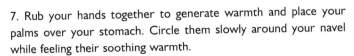

9. Put your fingers together so each palm is slightly cupped. Using both hands, pat your scalp from front to back, then pat your arms from shoulders to wrists. Continue to pat down your body. Include your chest, stomach, sides, buttocks, and down your legs.

10. When you have finished patting your body lightly all over, gently shake out your limbs and stretch them pleasantly. You have now completed the closing massage.

231

Qigong Breathing Exercises

Qigong Breathing Exercises combine regulated breathing and meditation. They simultaneously relax the body and develop the capacity for focused, yet relaxed, mental concentration. Some people find it difficult to start qigong because their restless minds cause them to become quickly impatient and bored. If this sounds like your dilemma, these exercises should be of help.

    Qigong Breathing Exercises can form a preliminary program to help calm and focus your mind before continuing on with moving forms of qigong practice. Yet they have healing power in their own right. Scientific research in China has shown that breathing exercises such as these benefit an array of chronic disorders related to the nervous system. They also reduce oxygen consumption and energy metabolism, thereby conserving energy and allowing the body to heal itself.

Follow the same guidelines for location and time as for the other qigong exercises. Place your body in a comfortable position. You may recline in a chair, lie down or use any other posture that feels comfortable to you.

Inhaling Peace, Relaxing Peace

1. Breathe normally and evenly through the nose. Allow your relaxed abdomen to rise and fall naturally with each breath.

2. Mentally say "inhaling peace" as you inhale and "relaxing peace" as you exhale. Develop an even, gentle rhythm of normal breathing that feels comfortable, while mentally repeating "inhaling peace" as you breathe in and "relaxing peace" as you breathe out.

3. When you feel ready, focus on your head as you imagine "inhaling peace" while inhaling and "relaxing peace" while exhaling. With your next breath, focus on your neck and inhale while mentally repeating "inhaling peace" and exhale while mentally saying "relaxing peace." Then focus on your shoulders and do the same. Continue in this way, through arms, hands, chest, back, abdomen, lower back, buttocks, legs and feet. You can then continue with the internal organs: heart, lungs, kidneys, stomach, liver, spleen, pancreas, intestines.

Pointer:
- You can modify the specific target sites as you choose. For example, you may choose to inhale into each shoulder, arm, or leg separately, or you may want to include knees, circulatory system, etc. The important point is to maintain relaxed breathing and mental focus as you go through this exercise.

Rhythmic Breathing

1. Breathe naturally through your nose. Allow the abdomen to expand as you inhale, and contract naturally as you exhale.

2. Pause for several seconds after each exhale, before starting the next inhale. During this pause, the lungs and body should feel completely relaxed and neutral. During each pause you should mentally say a phrase of your choice, such as "I'm calm." Pace the words evenly as if you are speaking to the beat of a metronome. ("I'm calm" = 2 beats.)

3. Gradually increase the duration of the pause between breaths until it is about 5-7 seconds and lengthen your mental phrase accordingly (i.e., "I feel calm" = 3 beats. "I feel peaceful" = 4 beats. "I feel calm and free" = 5 beats. "I feel calm and tranquil" = 6 beats.).

Pointer:

- *This exercise helps develop mental focus and concentration while effecting physiological changes associated with deepening tranquility. If you can feel the pulse of your heart beating through your relaxed body, you may find it helpful to pace the rhythm of your breaths and words by using your heartbeat as a metronome.*

Abdominal Breathing - Counting 20 Breaths

1. Breathe naturally through the nose. As you inhale, feel that you are bringing air all the way down to your belly and allow your abdomen to expand outward as it fills. As you exhale, allow your abdomen to collapse naturally like a deflating balloon. Breathe deeply, but do not strain or tense your muscles. Allow your breath to flow in a continuous motion of expansion and contraction, without pausing between outgoing and ingoing breaths.

2. Breathe calmly and deeply in this way until you are taking no more than 6 complete breaths per minute (that's approximately 5 seconds per inhale and 5 seconds per exhale). When you are comfortable with this, go on to the next step.

3. Count from one to twenty, counting one number for each breath cycle (inhale and exhale). Do not lose track of what number you are on. If your mind wanders and you lose track, start again from the beginning with "one." During the entire exercise, focus attention on your abdomen in the dan tian area just below the navel, and inward, almost to the center of your body. Do not try to pinpoint an exact spot; just maintain your attention on that general area.

Pointers:

- *Remember to follow the rise and fall of your abdomen. Remain as free from thoughts as possible. Don't be alarmed if at first your heart speeds up and you feel anxious about having to keep track of your counting - this is normal beginner's nerves; it will pass. If you find this exercise very difficult, begin with counting ten consecutive breaths and slowly work up to twenty.*

- *Whether you place your attention on moving the qi or moving the breath, remember to welcome it lovingly into your body. Feel its loving presence soothe and caress. This mental focus can help relieve pain and bring a smile to every cell in your body.*

A PARTING MESSAGE FROM MASTER WANG

Shing-ling-mei Wudang qigong can help you live a wonderful life. It can help your body be strong and healthy—and it can do more. Inside you is a feeling of deep peace and happiness. Shing-ling-mei can help you discover this place.

When you experience deep peace and calm, you can feel the qi of the universe. You can feel the qi of people around you and the qi of their situations. This generates understanding. Understanding inspires love and a desire to help others. When you love others, others are inspired to love you. When you help others, others become inspired to help you. By living in this way, your world becomes brighter.

Never forget to include yourself among those you love and help. You are responsible for yourself so learn to look after yourself in the kindest way. Pay attention to your schedule, your exercise, your body's diet and your mental diet. Nourish yourself with loving thoughts and feelings. Your body is a small universe existing within a larger universe. When you understand how to help your own small universe, you understand how to help the world.

I wish you each health and happiness as you travel your personal road through life.

Qing Chuan Wang

RESOURCES

FURTHER INFORMATION

For further information about *Shing-ling-mei* Wudang qigong, qi balancing, classes and workshops, visit our Web site at www.wudangqigong.com.

COMPANION DVD/VIDEO

A DVD companion to *Beautiful Heart, Beautiful Spirit* leads you through the six moving exercises described in this book. Master Wang demonstrates the movements as his wife, Katherine, narrates. Join Master Wang as he practices qigong in beautiful outdoor settings on his home island of Oahu, Hawaii. To order the DVD (also available as video cassette), visit our Web site at www.wudangqigong.com, or write to Companion DVD at the address below.

CONTACT MASTER WANG

The best resource a student can have is access to a living teacher. If you have questions or comments about this book, the exercises, or your experiences as you progress with qigong, you may contact Master Wang and he will respond.

Email: wudangqigong@hawaii.rr.com
Phone: 808 534-0452
Mailing address: Wudang Qigong
                      1519 Nuuanu Ave. #18
                      Honolulu, Hawaii, 96817 USA

CPSIA information can be obtained at www.ICGtesting.com
Printed in the USA
BVOW09s1302131016

464925BV00003B/56/P

9 780976 517801